ProgressionSeries

Medicine, Dentistry and Optometry

For entry to university and college in 2012

Published by: UCAS Rosehill New Barn Lane Cheltenham GL52 3LZ

Produced in conjunction with GTI Media Ltd

UCAS, a company limited by guarantee, is registered in England and Wales number: 2839815
Registered charity number: 1024741 (England and Wales) and SC038598 (Scotland)

UCAS reference number: PU036012
Publication reference: 11_081
ISBN: 978-1-84361-140-0
Price £15.99

We have made all reasonable efforts to ensure that the information in this publication was correct at time of publication. We will not, however, accept any liability for errors, omissions or changes to information since publication. Wherever possible any changes will be updated on the UCAS website (www.ucas.com).

UCAS and its trading subsidiary, UCAS Media Limited, accept advertising for publications that promote products and services relating to higher education and career progression. Revenue generated by advertising is invested by UCAS in order to enhance our applications services and to keep the cost to applicants as low as possible. Neither UCAS nor UCAS Media Limited endorse the products and services of other organisations that appear in this publication.

Further copies available from UCAS (p&p charges apply):

Contact Publication Services PO Box 130 Cheltenham GL52 3ZF

email: publicationservices@ucas.ac.uk or fax: 01242 544 806

For further information about the UCAS application process go to www.ucas.com.

If you need to contact us, details can be found at www.ucas.com/about_us/contact_us.

UCAS QUALITY AWARDS

Contents

Foreword

THINKING ABOUT MEDICINE, DENTISTRY AND OPTOMETRY?

Finding the course that's right for you at the right university or college can take time and it's important that you use all the resources available to you in making this important decision. We at UCAS have teamed up with GTI Media Ltd to provide you with *Progression to Medicine, Dentistry and Optometry* to show you how you can progress from being a student to careers in medicine, dentistry and optometry. You will find information on what the subject includes, entry routes and real-life case studies showing how it worked out for others.

Once you know which subject area you might be interested in, you can use the listings of all the full-time higher education courses in medicine, dentistry and optometry to see where you can study your subject. The course entry requirements are listed so you can check if getting in would be achievable for you. There's also advice on applying through UCAS, telling you what you need to know at each stage of the application process in just six easy steps to starting university or college.

We hope you find this publication helps you to choose and make your application to a course and university or college that is right for you.

On behalf of UCAS and GTI Media Ltd, I wish you every success in your research.

Mary Curnock Cook, Chief Executive, UCAS

www.ucas.com

at the heart of connecting people to higher education

Why medicine or dentistry?

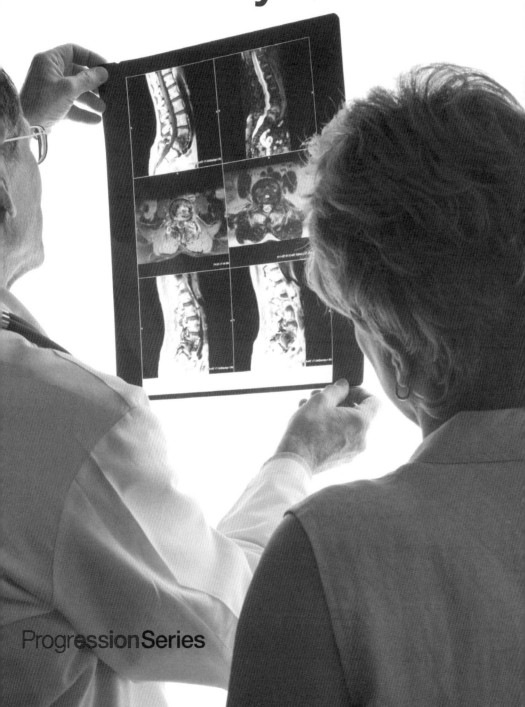

It could be you...

... reviving a stroke victim, then a partygoer who's had a bit too much to drink	– emergency medicine
... using image diagnostics to spot the sources of internal bleeding	– radiology
... going in and stopping the internal bleeding at its source	– surgery
... performing an emergency Caesarean section to save a baby's life	– obstetrics
... listening to a new mum struggling with postnatal depression	– psychiatry
... six colds, three pregnant mums and two cancer sufferers all in one afternoon	– GP
... ten fillings, three extractions, two bridges, five crowns	– dentist

... and lots more besides. From your first filling to your first child to your first bereavement, doctors and dentists will feature in your life as helpers, supporters and even lifesavers. Some you will meet only briefly for those one-off emergency or consultation encounters. Others, like your GP and family dentist, will be with you for longer. Could a career as a dentist or doctor be for you? The aim of this guide is to help you decide.

A CAREER IN MEDICINE OR DENTISTRY?

- A qualified GP employed by the NHS can earn between £53,781 and £81,158 – see **A career in medicine** on page 16.
- Over 70% of dentists are general dental practitioners – see **A career in dentistry** on page 24.
- As well as your academic ability, admissions tutors look for people skills, decisiveness, calmness under fire, attention to detail – see **The career for you?** on page 41.
- Qualifying as a doctor takes between 9 and 15 years full time – see **Routes to qualification** on page 54.

MEDICINE

Doctors play an essential role in the health and well-being of society. Medicine is one of the most respected careers and includes an enormous range of roles to choose from. Many doctors choose the profession for the chance to help people: it's very rewarding to play an important part in the recovery of the patients you encounter every day. And, as every patient is different, there are always challenges and you will never stop learning.

Medical training takes years of intensive study and practice, often at antisocial hours. However, once you are fully qualified you will be amply repaid and your skills will always be in demand – throughout the country or abroad.

DENTISTRY

People decide on dentistry for very different reasons. For some, it's the appeal of the 'fiddly' or the creative and aesthetic side of dentistry. For others, it's a more sociable option than medicine, since you get to form long-term relationships with your patients and provide them with continuing care. Sometimes, the decision is made for practical reasons: qualifying as a general practice dentist costs less than becoming a doctor and doesn't take as long as the medical route.

Whatever the reason, dentistry offers an increasingly broad range of career options, a stable future – since dentists are so much in demand in the UK – and a very flexible type of employment, as dentists can set their own working hours.

If you're interested in a possible career in medicine or dentistry, then this guide can help point you further in the right direction. Read on to discover:

- the main areas of work and roles on offer
- what it takes to be a doctor or a dentist
- how to get in and the paths to qualification
- advice from trainee and practising doctors and dentists.

Why medicine or dentistry?

Choose a career that is...

VARIED

There are few careers that offer as much variety as medicine or dentistry – both in the potential areas of work and your day-to-day experiences. Once you've chosen your specialism – and that includes being a GP or family dentist – new drugs and technology mean your career is constantly refreshed as you face new challenges and learn new techniques. And even if the medical problems are the same, the people affected by them can be very different.

VITAL TO SOCIETY

The NHS treats a spectacular number of people – on average 1 million every 24 hours. Every week NHS dentists see 700,000 patients, while GPs in Britain's more than 10,000 practices each see around 140 patients a week. The government budget in 2008/09 approximated to a contribution of £2,000 for each person in the UK. But the importance of the NHS isn't just a matter of statistics. How recently did someone in your family see a doctor or dentist? Or when did you last hear about someone making a miraculous recovery from illness, or benefiting from life-changing surgery, or even having a troublesome tooth removed? As a doctor or a dentist, you'll really make a difference.

TECHNICAL AND PEOPLE-FOCUSED

Many careers appeal because of the chance to develop technical expertise or to work with people. In medicine or dentistry you can lean towards one of these, but you will need a balance and interest in both. You'll use the latest drugs and technology, but you'll also see how these affect real people – your patients.

WELL PAID

It can be a long and expensive process to reach fully qualified status but the financial rewards make up for this. Both doctors and dentists receive above-average earnings throughout their careers. As a trainee doctor or dentist, your annual salary could be over £32,000, and consultants can earn between £74,000 and £176,000. Check out the salary levels on page 18 (medicine) and page 25 (dentistry) for more information.

SECURE IN THE LONG TERM

People will always get ill, break their legs playing football or have problems with their teeth, so your skills, knowledge and expertise will always be in demand. Both medicine and dentistry have clearly structured career paths and you won't necessarily be tied to one hospital, practice or location either. There are 167 NHS acute trusts and 58 mental health NHS trusts as well as 250 private-sector hospitals in the UK, many of which are national centres of excellence for different specialisms, so you can work anywhere in the country.

WHAT DO GRADUATES SAY?

The best part of my job is the people – both the patients and my colleagues. It is uniquely satisfying to take away pain and to help someone to have a healthier mouth.
Anna Maxwell, dental practitioner

Being a practical person, optometry suits me perfectly. Optometry is a career in which you never stop learning and helping other people, and I love that.
Ina Jarre, optometrist

As a doctor, people look up to you for help and advice when they are at their most vulnerable. This is a huge responsibility, but it also means that you can make a real difference to their lives.
Martin Slattery, final year medical student

Which area?

Find out more about each profession before you make your choice.

MEDICINE

Doctors use the science of medicine – the knowledge of how our bodies and minds work – to help people deal with disease, pain and ill health.

What types of doctors are there?

There are over 60 medical specialities available to doctors once they have completed their general medical training. They have many requirements and characteristics in common, but some require particular skills, such as manual dexterity for surgery, and each requires doctors to take specialist exams. Each speciality is governed by a Royal College or Faculty, which sets the entry and training requirements and the specialist membership and fellowship exams. (See **Which specialism?** on page 19.)

Where could you work?

There are nearly 240,000 registered doctors in the UK, the vast majority of whom are employed in the NHS. However, many (particularly fully qualified consultants) now also work either exclusively in private-sector hospitals or across both the public and private sectors. NHS doctors will work either in a hospital (for example, as an orthopaedic surgeon) or in a community setting (for example, as a general practitioner). An alternative route is to be sponsored by the armed forces as an Army, RAF or Royal Navy medical officer. Your fees and salary will be paid throughout your training in exchange for a commitment to a minimum period of service, after which you can decide to stay or leave.

DENTISTRY

Dentists are healthcare professionals who are experts in the diagnosis and treatment of a range of problems affecting the mouth and teeth. The most effective dentists combine strong diagnostic, clinical and social skills.

Where do they work?

General dental practice: Armed with a BDS (degree in dentistry) and one year's practical postgraduate training in an approved practice (known as vocational training), you could become a general dental practitioner in a local family or community practice.

It's usual to work as an associate in someone else's practice before being able to set up on your own.

Later on you could become a practice owner (principal) by becoming a partner, buying a practice or establishing a new practice. Once you've completed your training, you're pretty much up and running, and there are no higher grades or levels. This can be perceived as a relative lack of career progression, but the upside is that you can further your knowledge at your own pace and follow the particular dental specialities that interest you. And dentists start to earn good money much sooner than their medical colleagues. (However, their medical colleagues can overtake them on their way to a consultant position.)

As a general dental practitioner (GDP) you may practise under the NHS or privately. Many dentists opt for a mixture of NHS and private work. In private practice you are likely to perform a higher proportion of cosmetic dentistry alongside the more routine work. Under a system introduced in England and Wales in April 2006, payment for NHS work is based on the amount of treatment carried out by each practice or practitioner.

Private fees are set by each dentist individually and may vary according to the particular practice. As a GDP you are self-employed and run your own business.

The armed forces: The Defence Dental Services sponsor a number of dental trainees through their undergraduate and vocational training and pay a salary to dental trainees in exchange for a commitment to work in the forces as a dentist for a certain period of time (for example, six years). Dentists in the armed forces hold a commissioned rank and have a very structured career path. The salary structure during the vocational period is different from that for the other options outlined on this page. For more information visit the Defence Dental Services website at **www.mod.uk/DefenceInternet/microsite/dms.**

Hospital dentistry: There are many specialisms if you go down this route, including orthodontics (bone structure), periodontics (gums) and surgical dentistry. Dental departments of large general hospitals have the facilities to offer treatment that may not be available or feasible in your local practice. You will tend to see fewer patients than in general practice but their treatment is likely to be more complex. Rather than doing a year of vocational training to become a GDP, you will have to take the medical training route. There is a defined salary structure, career structure and training pathway for hospital dentists and you will need to obtain recognised postgraduate qualifications in order to advance.

Community Dental Service (CDS): Dentists working
for a CDS provide care for patients with particular
needs: for example, elderly housebound people or those
with mental or physical disabilities. To become a
community dental officer a graduate must also
complete a period of vocational training. As in hospital
dentistry, posts are salaried. There is a defined career
structure and opportunities for managerial and research
duties.

Introducing medicine

ProgressionSeries

A career in medicine

This section aims to give you an overview of the main career choices, specialisms, working conditions and pay for doctors in the UK today.

If you have an interest in science and a desire to help people, then a career in medicine could be for you. At this stage in your career you don't need to decide on a particular specialism; most medical students specialise only once they've had more exposure to the different fields of medicine during their medical course.

HOSPITAL DOCTOR OR GENERAL PRACTITIONER (GP)?

The most obvious choice for trainee doctors is whether to work in a hospital or in general practice. GPs generally work under less pressure, can take a more holistic approach to the treatment of their patients, and earn more pay early on. On the other hand, hospital doctors are at the leading edge, making an immediate impact on their patients' lives. The following chart sums up some of the key differences between the two roles.

HOSPITAL DOCTOR	GP
Mostly employed in NHS hospitals serving vast regional or even national populations; many also now work across public and private sectors	Mostly employed in NHS local communities, serving a much smaller base of local people
More likely to be specialist	More likely to be generalist
One-off patient contact; sees patients for short intense periods	Ongoing patient contact; gets to know patients over time
Hospital-based	Surgery-based
Aspires to 'consultant', ie top expert in their specialism	Aspires to GP principal, ie senior partner in their practice

Working conditions

Flexible options such as job share, shared on-call, and part-time working are now available to trainee doctors once they have completed their university course. This makes a medical career much more appealing to people who previously might have opted out of medicine due to the long working hours. This said, part-time work is more readily available in some specialities than others. Working hours for junior doctors were reduced to 56 hours per week in 2007, thanks to the EU Working Time Directive, and reduced further to 48 hours in 2009. However the work is still highly pressurised in some specialisms due to patient targets and altered working patterns.

Pay

For hospital doctors, pay builds from a modest beginning to great financial rewards as they near the top of their profession, while GPs typically earn more money more quickly. The pay scales overleaf apply to public sector doctors at different levels and stages of their careers.

TYPICAL SCALES

POSITION	TYPICAL PAY
Hospital	
Foundation year one trainee	£22,412
Foundation year two trainee	£27,798
Doctor in specialist training	£36,807 - £70,126
Consultant	£74,504 - £100,446
GP	
Qualified salaried GP (NHS)	£53,781 - £81,158
Independent GP (those who are self-employed and hold contracts either on their own or in a partnership with their local PCT)	£80,000 - £120,000

Source: NHS Careers website **www.nhscareers.nhs.uk**

Which specialism?

With over 60 different specialist medical training programmes, there's something for everyone.

In theory, the range of programmes offers junior doctors a wealth of fields to choose from. In practice, however, many areas of medicine are oversubscribed and competition to get in is very intense. Broadly speaking, hospital specialisms fall into two main groups: medical and surgical.

Medical work involves diagnosis and non-surgical treatments. Many of the specialities focus on particular organs, such as the heart (cardiology), or diseases, such as cancer (oncology).

Surgical work involves the in-theatre specialists, who operate on the body to address injury or disease.

However, some specialisms, such as psychiatry and gynaecology, don't really sit in either of these two main groups.

Examples of the most popular specialist fields, and what they involve, are outlined below.

EMERGENCY MEDICINE
(FORMERLY ACCIDENT & EMERGENCY OR A&E)

The work
Emergency services provide immediate care to the acutely ill and injured, ranging from major trauma and medical emergencies to a large volume of minor injuries and complaints.

The conditions

The unpredictability of cases, the need to call on different medical knowledge from one case to another, the distress of patients, plus the demands of meeting government waiting-list targets all make this a pressurised environment, so you'll need nerves of steel.

The upside

There is the opportunity to make a real, immediate difference to ease someone's pain. It is the only place in the hospital that offers experience in such a breadth of medicine.

The downside

You may be exposed to patients with violent behaviour from drug or alcohol abuse, and there are also potential demands for out-of-hours shift work.

For more info

The College of Emergency Medicine
www.collemergencymed.ac.uk

OBSTETRICS & GYNAECOLOGY

The work

This specialism includes such diverse aspects as gynaecological oncology (eg treating cervical cancer), treating menopause, in vitro fertilisation (IVF), and foetal monitoring and surgery. On the obstetrics side, the doctor is responsible for the care of **two** patients simultaneously – mother and baby – spending a lot of time looking after women who are not ill but who are experiencing a major life event.

The conditions

This area of work is characterised by extreme highs and lows, especially on the obstetrics side. You may also find yourself under pressure if you're the only specialist registrar capable of performing a Caesarean section on a ward.

The upside

It's one of the few fields that allows doctors to maintain an interest in both medicine and surgery.

The downside

There is so much riding on the successful delivery of one little life.

For more info

Royal College of Obstetricians and Gynaecologists
www.rcog.org.uk

PSYCHIATRY

The work

Mental illness is one of the biggest health problems in the UK. As the guardians of mental health, psychiatrists treat a whole range of medical conditions including depression, learning disabilities, eating disorders, drug and alcohol abuse, phobias and post-traumatic stress disorders, as well as helping people cope with emotional and stressful situations such as a bereavement or family trauma. It's an odd mix of intense one-to-one work and teamwork, as psychiatrists work in multidisciplinary teams with a variety of other healthcare professionals such as social workers. It is also possible to specialise in areas including child psychiatry and forensic psychiatry (working in a criminal or legal context, to treat and assess offenders).

The conditions

You could find yourself working in a variety of settings, such as care homes, secure psychiatric units, community centres and even prisons. It's also a field where flexible working options are readily accepted.

The upside

If you're a 'people' person, psychiatry brings you directly into the very real human side of medicine and medical care.

The downside

It can seem thankless as it can take a very long time to begin to see the effect of your work. In this field, remember that you're in it for the long haul.

For more info

The Royal College of Psychiatrists
www.rcpsych.ac.uk

RADIOLOGY

The work

A radiologist focuses on the use of imaging to diagnose, treat and monitor disease. Ever-clearer imaging quality is creating more opportunities to offer image-guided treatment, sometimes without the need for surgical intervention. For this kind of work, a good knowledge of general medicine and surgery is paramount. The massive growth in uses of radiological imaging has resulted in a worldwide shortage of trained radiologists.

The conditions

As most of the work is lab-based, doctors work individually and intensively on their own, and then interact with surgeons and specialists from numerous fields of medicine to give their findings and work out a treatment plan.

The upside

It's rewarding to spot disease early enough to treat it, thanks to attention to detail and improved image quality.

The downside

Long, intense hours examining x-rays and scan results can be hard on your eyesight.

For more info

The Royal College of Radiologists
www.rcr.ac.uk

SURGERY

The work

In-theatre specialists spend their training years in general surgery and specialise as consultants in one or two fields, for instance reconstruction/plastic, maxillofacial, colorectal and vascular surgery. Contrary to popular perception, surgeons do not spend the majority of their time in theatre. The average surgeon spends approximately 1.5 days per week in theatre, and the rest of their time on ward rounds and running outpatient clinics to follow up with patients.

The conditions

Working conditions get easier as you go higher up the career ladder – but if you have a full theatre list, expect very early starts and long days.

The upside

Surgery really suits the pragmatic and dynamic medic. You don't have to deal so much with the patient, and success (or failure) is more immediately apparent.

The downside

It is a highly pressured specialism with no margin for error.

For more info

The Royal College of Surgeons (England)
www.rcseng.ac.uk

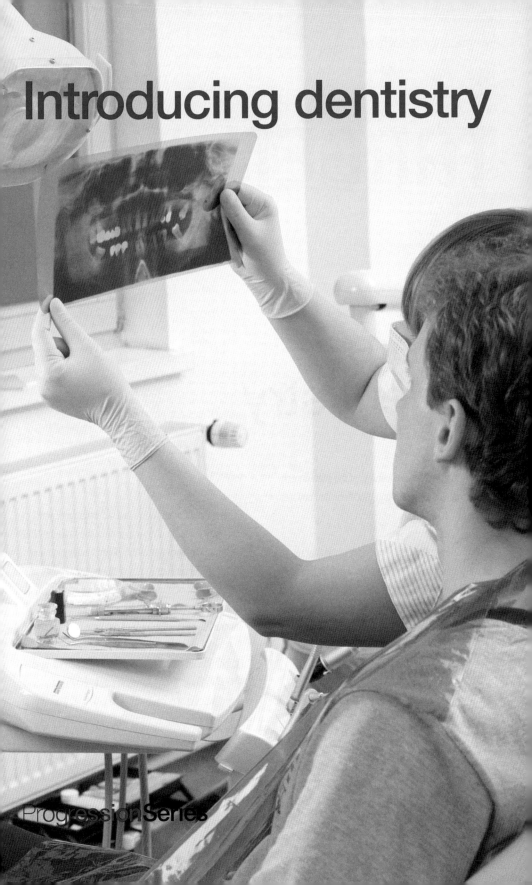

Introducing dentistry

A career in dentistry

This section provides an overview of the main career choices, specialisms, working conditions and pay for dentists in the UK today.

Compared to their medical colleagues, the majority of dental graduates have a much more straightforward career structure, since most dental students go into general dental practice. The number of dental options may be more limited, but those that exist are highly specialised.

PAY

General dental practitioners are self-employed, and from April 2006 received a 'per item' fee from the NHS; the system of payments to NHS dentists in England and Wales is now one based on contracts. The amount of money paid to dentists under these contracts is based on an assessment of the typical amount of work done by the practice or practitioner over one year.

Hospital-based dental specialists are paid according to NHS salary guidelines. Although pay levels may be lower during training, a consultant will receive a very generous income.

TYPICAL SALARIES

POSITION	TYPICAL PAY
Hospital	
Foundation year two trainee	£27,798
Specialist registrar	£29,705–£46,708
Dental consultant	£74,504–£100,446
General Practice	
Vocational dental practitioner (VDP) during their vocational training year	£29,800
Community dental officer	£37,714–£80,674

Source: NHS Careers website **www.nhscareers.nhs.uk**

Which specialism?

The vast majority of dental students become general dental practitioners (GDPs), but it is possible to become a specialist.

To specialise in dentistry usually means you'll have to follow the hospital dentistry route. Once qualified, it is entirely possible (and even common in some specialisms) for the dental specialist to move out of the hospital setting to establish their own practice – for example, in orthodontics. The key dental specialisms are outlined below.

GENERAL DENTAL PRACTITIONER

The work
Most graduate dentists become general dental practitioners in public and (increasingly) private dental practices in local communities, treating all ages and all general dental complaints from fillings to extractions to bridges to crowns – and some cosmetic surgery.

The conditions
Despite the pressures of dental emergencies and the limited resources from the NHS, general dental practitioners usually have a good work-life balance. They get to decide when, where and for how long they work; they start to earn a high salary quite soon after graduation; and they have a high degree of autonomy, especially if they run their own practice.

The upside
There's a great deal of people contact and you can build up long-term relationships with clients.

The downside
Opportunities for career progression are limited once you've become partner in a practice.

For more info
Faculty of General Dental Practice
www.fgdp.org.uk

ORTHODONTICS

The work

Orthodontics is the branch of dentistry concerned with growth of the face, development of the 'occlusion' (alignment of the upper and lower jaw) and the correction and prevention of occlusal abnormalities. These are the dental specialists responsible for that brace you might have worn as a child to correct protruding or badly aligned teeth.

The conditions

Qualified orthodontists are likely to begin working in a specialist practice with more experienced colleagues, or may choose to establish a new practice (which is more complicated than setting up a general dental practice). They may provide treatment in the NHS or privately, or a mix of both. Hours of work will then be of their choosing and, like general dental practitioners, they will have a high-quality lifestyle with limited pressure.

The upside

There's opportunity for longer, more intricate, one-to-one treatments, and satisfaction from helping patients overcome conditions about which they are often self-conscious.

The downside

Orthodontic treatments take time, so you'll need a lot of patience.

For more info
British Orthodontic Society
www.bos.org.uk

SPECIALITIES

Other 'dontics' dental specialities include: **periodontics** (treatment of gums); **endodontics** (treatment of the tooth root and surrounding tissue); and **prosthodontics** (replacement of missing teeth by prostheses). At present there is no special funding for trainees in these specialities, so the majority of trainees will be self-funding, and most will probably enter private practice.

For more information see:

British Society of Periodontology
www.bsperio.org.uk

British Endodontic Society
www.britishendodonticsociety.org

Association of Consultants and Specialists in Restorative Dentistry
www.restdent.org.uk

ORAL AND MAXILLOFACIAL SURGERY

The work

Nicknamed 'maxfax', this is a unique specialism as surgeons must possess both a dental and a medical degree, as well as being on the Dental Register and having the requisite surgical qualifications. This speciality has its origins in wartime, when dental surgeons became prominent in devising local flap reconstruction of lost facial tissues. The core activity of the speciality is the management of facial trauma, both soft and hard tissue. Approximately 80% of mouth and jaw cancer is currently managed by this speciality, which also covers congenital abnormalities, such as a cleft palate.

The conditions

'Maxfax' surgeons work in acute general hospitals, specialist hospitals and university teaching hospitals. They typically spend more time in theatre and on local anaesthesia operations than generalist surgeons. The work is a combination of emergencies and acute cases, plus follow-ups, or minor and aesthetic work carried out on an outpatient basis. The schedule for trainees also involves night and weekend 'on calls'.

The upside

It has the most visible results of all surgery specialities – on the face.

The downside

'Maxfax' has the longest, most demanding training requirements – starting with a dental and a medical degree.

For more info

The British Association of Oral and Maxillofacial Surgeons
www.baoms.org.uk

SURGICAL DENTISTRY

The work

This area of work deals with the diagnosis and surgical management of anomalies of the teeth and their supporting structures. In other words, surgical dentists work exclusively inside the mouth itself. Extracting wisdom teeth is a common procedure.

The conditions

Treatment is normally carried out on an outpatient basis under local anaesthesia, so it generally fits into a regular working day. Surgical dentists may also work in specialist practice, hospitals or a community dental service. If working in a hospital, they may be employed as associate specialists under the supervision of a

consultant in oral and maxillofacial surgery and, as a result, may get to take on a wider clinical role.

The upside

For those who still want to combine surgery with dentistry, the route to qualification is quicker than for maxillofacial surgery.

The downside

Once you qualify, you'll still be restricted to working within the mouth and won't be able to work more widely on the head, face or neck.

For more info

British Association of Oral Surgeons
www.baos.org.uk

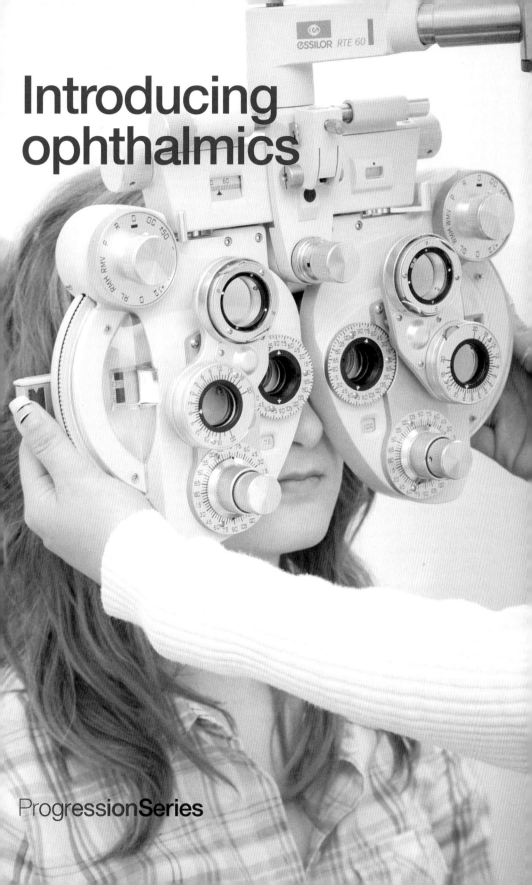

Introducing
ophthalmics

Progression**Series**

It could be you...

... carrying out laser eye surgery using the latest technology — ophthalmologist

... diagnosing common health conditions such as diabetes and glaucoma — optometrist

... helping a child overcome their squint — orthoptist

... and lots more besides. Could a degree in an ophthalmics-related subject be for you? The aim of this section is to help you decide.

Why ophthalmics?

Sight is undoubtedly one of our most precious
senses. Can you imagine life without it? It is vital for so
many aspects of what we do: at work, at home, driving,
for sports, at leisure. By working in an ophthalmics field
you will be making a huge and often immediate
difference to your patients.

In this section of the book we will take a look at
careers in the following fields: ophthalmology, optometry
and orthoptics. Read on to find out about what each
area involves, the working environment, typical salaries,
career prospects and training requirements.

Ophthalmologists

WHAT DO OPHTHALMOLOGISTS DO?

Ophthalmology is a speciality within medicine that focuses on the medical and surgical management of conditions that affect the eye, the area around it and vision as a whole. The eye and its health can be affected by a wide variety of things including injury, cataracts, diabetes, and congenital (existing at birth) and genetic problems. This means that ophthalmologists treat patients of all ages and backgrounds, from babies to pensioners.

Ophthalmologists must first qualify as a doctor and then undertake further training to specialise in the diagnosis and treatment of eye diseases and conditions. They can prescribe glasses and drugs and will also perform traditional and/or laser eye surgery. Some ophthalmologists will train further to specialise in such

areas as retinal disease, corneal disease, glaucoma, muscle problems, neural disorders, tumours, plastic surgery and pathology.

One of the main advantages of dealing with the eye is that much of it is transparent, which enables the ophthalmologist to observe its structures and abnormalities directly, which is not possible for many other parts of the human body. The ability to restore someone's sight, by removing cataracts, for example, is one of the most rewarding aspects of the job.

THE WORKING ENVIRONMENT

When compared with other medical specialities, working hours are pretty good. While your clinics and theatre sessions will be very busy, there isn't much out-of-hours work. Trainees receive a lot of guidance from consultants and doctors, and will be supported by allied professionals such as ophthalmic nurses, optometrists and orthopists.

CAREER PROSPECTS

Ophthalmology offers a challenging career with a fascinating and fast-developing combination of surgical, laser and medical treatments to help patients. Most conditions that cause reduced eyesight are more common in old age and, with an increasingly elderly population, the Royal College of Ophthalmologists expects the need for highly trained ophthalmologists in the UK to grow in the coming years.

The field of ophthalmology is fast-moving in terms of knowledge and techniques; even as recently as a few years ago cataract surgery wasn't as common as it is today. Laser surgery is becoming increasingly common and is used to perform outpatient procedures, such as correction of short-sightedness.

Improvements in microsurgical instrumentation have led to the development of procedures not considered possible as little as a decade ago. New advances in genetic analysis mean that gene therapy will be a reality in the future. Other technological developments will continue to improve future treatment and management of people with current or potential visual impairment.

ROUTES TO QUALIFICATION

Medical degree

Ophthalmologists must train as doctors before specialising, so you will need to study for a medical degree if this career area appeals. To read more about medicine, refer to the beginning of this book. After completing your undergraduate degree and two foundation years in general medicine, you can specialise in ophthalmology. This will involve undertaking rigorous specialist training as detailed below.

Specialist training

Specialist training in ophthalmology takes about seven years. During the first two years, you will be expected to acquire the general clinical skills of an ophthalmologist, as well as a basic knowledge of the conditions covered by the specialism, and you can gain first-hand experience of extra-ocular procedures in clinics and theatre sessions. You can carry out supervised intraocular surgery once you have more experience and have attended the Royal College of Ophthalmologists' course in basic microsurgical skills.

Over the next five years, you will rotate through each part of the required curriculum, spending around six months in each specialism. You will need to gain a certificate of eligibility for higher specialist training from the Royal College of Ophthalmologists to do this part of the training, as well as passing the MCROphth, or equivalent. At the end of this, the norm is to undertake a fellowship in your chosen subspeciality before going on to a consultant post.

Advanced subspecialist training in ophthalmology

Once you have completed your training in ophthalmology, you can go on to train for another year in a subspeciality. One attraction of this is that training can be undertaken anywhere, from Australia and New Zealand to Africa and Asia.

WHAT SKILLS DO YOU NEED?

Apart from the extensive medical training you will need to undertake, ophthalmologists need to show evidence that they possess the following personal qualities:

- good manual/dexterity skills
- good vision
- the ability to use instruments competently and comfortably
- good communication skills to deal with patients of a variety of ages, backgrounds and in different levels of health
- teamworking skills.

FURTHER INFORMATION

www.rcophth.ac.uk
The Royal College of Ophthalmologists

Optometrists

WHAT DO OPTOMETRISTS DO?

Optometrists, or dispensing opticians, look after the visual health of their patients, thereby helping to maintain or improve the quality of their lives. They are primary health care specialists, trained to examine the eyes and discover any visual problems, proof of injury, ocular diseases or abnormality and problems with general health.

Did you know that a thorough eye examination can reveal such conditions as high blood pressure or diabetes? Optometrists can detect such diseases and offer advice on what to do next.

Most people who see an optometrist will not have a serious health problem. The main reasons they go are for eye tests and check-ups and to buy prescription glasses or contact lenses. If a problem cannot be resolved by an optometrist, referral for further investigation may be necessary.

THE WORKING ENVIRONMENT

Optometrists work in a variety of settings, from a high-street chain or independent practice to a hospital eye department or in research or teaching.

How much you earn will depend on where you work and how qualified you are. See the box overleaf for a guide to salaries in private and public practice.

	PRIVATE PRACTICE	NHS HOSPITAL OR CLINIC
Pre-registration year	c. £16,500	£18,152
Starting salaries	£19,000 – £28,000	£25,472 – £34,189
Senior-level salaries	£37,000 – £53,000	Optometrist consultant: £54,454 – £80,810

One of the main attractions of the job is its good working hours. Optometrists working in either private practice or in a hospital can usually expect to work 36 to 39 hours per week, between 9am and 5.30pm. Saturday, and sometimes Sunday, work is common in private practice but you will have a day off in the week in lieu.

You will need to be happy with working for extended periods of time in small, darkened consulting rooms with no natural light. If you have ever had an eye examination you will know that the job requires optometrists to make close physical contact with people when examining their eyes, and this can involve a lot of bending and standing.

CAREER PROSPECTS

Once qualified, optometrists can pursue a specialism such as paediatrics, contact lenses, low vision and sports vision. Some optometrists, for example, work for practices that specialise in these fields or in other areas such as behavioural optometry or learning difficulties. A few optometrists are also employed by private laser eye adjustment centres that use different technical measuring devices from those used in most practices.

However, generally speaking, an optometrist's role will not change dramatically throughout their career, although of course they will become more experienced and faster at testing with time. Senior optometrists will enjoy similar types of work to their more junior counterparts, although other opportunities can open up, such as running their own practice. Practice management can prove to be very lucrative for optometrists, who will have to juggle their management responsibilities with their routine optometry work.

If you choose to work in a hospital environment instead, career progression can be more structured as the NHS has a defined career grade structure for hospital optometrists, with a corresponding salary scale. One of the major attractions of optometry as a career is that it offers employees flexibility in terms of full- or part-time working to match their other commitments and responsibilities.

ROUTES TO QUALIFICATION

Optometry degree

You cannot qualify as an optometrist without completing an undergraduate degree in optometry at one of the General Optical Council's (GOC) approved universities, which are:

- Anglia Ruskin University
- Aston University
- University of Bradford
- Cardiff University
- City University
- Glasgow Caledonian University
- University of Manchester
- University of Ulster.

With only eight universities offering the course in the UK, competition for entry is understandably fierce. Average A level grades of AAB are expected and should be in science-based subjects such as biology, chemistry, physics or mathematics. Some universities will accept a non-science subject as a third A level or, instead, two AS levels. You should contact the individual institutions for advice and information on their particular entry requirements. If you are interested in studying optometry but do not have science A levels, Aston University offers a foundation course (Year Zero) to compensate for this.

If you do not obtain a minimum 2.2 class of degree, you will need to complete the General Optical Council's optometry progression scheme to continue your training.

Pre-registration training

The next step is to complete a pre-registration year, involving full-time clinical experience as a trainee under the supervision of a registered optometrist. This year enables you to develop the knowledge and theory gained at university and apply this practically in a work-based setting. At the end of your course, you will need to prove that you have covered all of the General Optical Council's Stage 2 core competencies to the satisfaction of the College of Optometrists' appointed assessor.

You must then pass the Final Assessment examinations, including practical examinations and a clinical decision-making section based on case studies. At this point you can register as an optometrist with the GOC.

WHAT SKILLS DO YOU NEED?

As well as high levels of academic achievement and professional knowledge, you will also need to show evidence that you possess the following skills and qualities:

- **communication skills** – you must be able to communicate effectively with a wide range of people from all backgrounds
- **interpersonal skills** – to put anxious patients at ease and be comfortable yourself about working in close proximity with them
- **theoretical and practical skills** – the ability to understand and apply scientific principles and methods
- **technical skills** – you must be comfortable using complex equipment
- **manual dexterity and accuracy** – when dealing with patients
- **good organisational and administrative skills** – to maintain patients' records and appointments
- **research skills** – to stay on top of scientific and technological developments in your field.

Competition for pre-registration positions has increased so gaining work experience in an optician's can be very helpful, either during weekends or on one of the summer programmes offered by some of the larger high-street chains for students between their second and third years.

FURTHER INFORMATION

www.ioo.org.uk The Institute of Optometry
www.optical.org The General Optical Council
www.college-optometrists.org
The College of Optometrists

Orthoptists

WHAT DO ORTHOPTISTS DO?

Orthoptists diagnose and treat problems with vision and abnormalities of eye movement and eye position. They carry out tests to diagnose problems and determine how these should be managed. The type of problems they deal with include:

- ocular motility (eye movement)
- binocular vision (seeing with both eyes)
- amblyopia (lazy eye)
- strabismus (squint).

As is the case with ophthalmologists and optometrists, orthoptists work with a wide range of patients, of all ages and from all backgrounds, to help improve their quality of life. Typical tasks include:

- receiving patient referrals from the eye casualty department, eye clinics, neurology, GPs, health visitors and community clinics
- investigating the patient's vision, eye position and eye movement, through observation and by using specialist equipment
- drawing up treatment plans for patients, which could involve surgery, or using more traditional treatments such as using eye patches to correct lazy eyes
- explaining the diagnosis and treatment procedure to a patient
- participating in specialist clinics for such conditions as glaucoma, low vision and strokes

- liaising with occupational therapists, physiotherapists and nursing staff
- dealing with general administrative duties relating to patient care
- teaching students on placement and other health professionals, eg GPs and optometry students.

THE WORKING ENVIRONMENT

Orthoptists are normally employed by the NHS, and salaries can vary between different trusts. The recommended starting salary for newly qualified orthoptists is £20,710 (basic grade) to £26,839. More experienced, specialist and advanced orthoptists can earn anything between £24,831 and £39,273. Heads of department typically earn £37,996 to £65,657. Additional allowances are allocated to people living and working in London.

You will normally work within a hospital clinic, although many orthoptists visit community clinics and health centres and work in primary schools and schools for children with special needs. While private practice is possible, it is rare and would need to occur alongside an ophthalmologist.

Job flexibility is common within this area, with career breaks, flexitime, part-time working and job shares possible. Most people working within this field are female but increasingly more men are applying. Positions can be found all over the UK but are most common in large hospitals and cities.

ROUTES TO QUALIFICATION

An approved orthoptics degree, from either Sheffield or Liverpool universities, is essential for state registration and in order to practise as an orthoptist. Both of these universities require at least five GCSE passes at grades A–C and three A levels, preferably in science subjects; check with the institutions before applying.

Both Liverpool and Sheffield offer 40 places each year but, with over 600 applications, competition is fierce. While prior work experience is not essential, it will prove that you are committed to and understand the profession, which could help your chances of gaining a place.

Orthoptics degrees incorporate theory with practice. During the three years of study, you will undertake numerous clinical placements in various orthoptic departments throughout the UK under the supervision of a clinical tutor. The first year of study will give you the necessary scientific information to understand the visual system, together with an introduction to optics and orthoptics. In the second and third years, you will learn about investigation and the management of binocular vision disorders.

WHAT SKILLS DO YOU NEED?

It can be helpful to have pre-entry work experience in either a paid or voluntary capacity. This could include helping out at a nursery, or working with the elderly or with disabled children or adults. You will also need to show that you possess the following skills:

- good communication and empathetic skills to deal with both patients and fellow professionals
- the ability to work alone or as part of a team
- patience
- self-motivation and initiative
- attention to detail
- organisational skills.

The general advice is to ask the head orthoptist at your local eye hospital if you could arrange to sit in at one of their clinics. They will normally be more than happy to help provided enough notice is given.

The NHS pays for orthoptics students' fee contribution. You may also receive a means-tested bursary to help towards living costs but places are limited so you need to apply early. If you cannot secure funding through the NHS, you will need to look for other funding sources.

FURTHER INFORMATION

The British and Irish Orthoptic Society
www.orthoptics.org.uk

The career
for you?

ProgressionSeries

Is medicine, dentistry or ophthalmics for you?

Being a successful doctor, dentist or opthalmologist calls for more than an in-depth understanding of the relevant science. It also requires certain skills and personal qualities or attributes.

To help you decide if a career in the medical, dental or ophthalmics-related profession is for you, we suggest you consider the following questions:

- What do you want from your future work?
- What does the course typically involve?
- Which skills do doctors and dentists typically need?

WHAT DO YOU WANT FROM YOUR FUTURE WORK?

You may not have an answer for this now, but your current studies, work experience to date and even your hobbies can help give you clues about the kind of work you enjoy, and the skills you have already started to develop. Start with a blank sheet of paper and note down the answers to the questions we've provided on the following page to help get you thinking. Be as brutally honest with yourself as you can. Don't write what you think will impress your teachers or parents; write what really matters to you and you'll start to see a pattern emerge.

ANSWERING THESE QUESTIONS MAY HELP YOU CHOOSE YOUR CAREER

- When you think of your future, in what kind of environment do you see yourself working: office, outdoor, nine-to-five, high-pressure, regular routine?
- What are your favourite hobbies outside school? What is it about them you enjoy? Working with people? Finding out how things work?
- What are your favourite subjects in school?

- What is it about them that you enjoy most? Being able to create something, debating, problem solving, practical hands-on work? What do you dislike about the other subjects you're studying?
- Which aspects of your work experience have you most enjoyed?

WHAT DOES THE COURSE TYPICALLY INVOLVE?

Course intensity: It's especially important for medical students to know that the first stage of your studies – the undergraduate degree – will require great stamina, as it's typically five years of intensive studying for exams, plus numerous in-hospital placements or 'rotations'. So if you don't see yourself spending hours studying when your friends on other courses have long since left for the day or the weekend, or have even completed their course and are off earning money, then maybe medicine is not for you. Would-be dentists should also know that much of the course is now chemistry-based (you'll study biochemistry), as well as the expected courses on anatomy, physiology and pathology, and dental materials science. Ophthalmology training will be as long and intensive as medical training, while optometry and orthoptics courses are shorter.

Course structure: All courses are a combination of **academic** (ie studying sciences) work and **clinical** (ie hands-on, in hospital or clinics) work. Most universities now mix the two. But others (most notably Oxford and Cambridge) split the course, with the first two to three years spent in the classroom and on lecture-based academic work, studying sciences, and the latter two to three years spent on placements or 'rotations' in hospitals.

In addition, some institutions are increasing the amount of **self-directed learning** (where students are given a task, a list of objectives, and told to go away and research it, then come back to discuss what they've found out).

Some courses also offer an **'intercalated'** degree, which includes the chance to take one to two years out to study another science-related subject in the middle of your medical or dental degree. This is of most value to students who identify early on that they want to specialise, particularly in a research field.

It's important to find out how much of the course teaching is lecture-based, self-directed and hands-on, and if it offers an intercalated option. This will mean you can choose the option that suits you best.

WHICH SKILLS DO MEDICAL, DENTAL AND OPHTHALMIC-RELATED PROFESSIONALS TYPICALLY NEED?

Without doubt, admissions tutors look for **strong academic ability** – just to prove your ability to cope with the straight science, plus clear **evidence of a commitment to medicine, dentistry or ophthalmics** as a career (which can usually be demonstrated through work experience placements). Beyond this, the following key skills are required:

- excellent communication skills – speaking and listening – to be able to explain complicated medical concepts in ordinary language, and to draw out crucial information from patients, often when they're under stress, and to put patients at their ease
- empathy – a degree of sensitivity and understanding of each patient's situation and feelings. Dentists, in particular, need to have strong 'people' skills, as you'll be providing dental care for people of all ages and you'll be seeing them on an ongoing basis
- problem-solving ability – the ability quickly to assess and analyse a situation or case
- attention to detail – the ability to pick up on the smallest of signs or symptoms
- calmness under fire – mostly for hospital doctors. Given the combination of long hours and unpredictability of cases, you've got to be able to cope under pressure
- confidentiality – knowing what to communicate, when and to whom
- stamina – to cope with the 12-hour shifts and the on-call work
- decisiveness – to be able to back your own judgement and make decisions quickly
- of course, in all these fields it helps to have a steady hand and minimum squeamishness.

Alternative careers

If the traditional doctor, dentist or ophthalmic roles don't feel quite 'you', but you still have a strong leaning towards science and healthcare, there are many roles in related fields to choose from.

Below are some of the main related professions.

ALLIED HEALTH PROFESSIONS

These are the professionals who work alongside doctors and dentists to help transform lives in all sorts of ways. Examples include physiotherapists, speech and language therapists, paramedics and dietitians. You may want to consider reading *Progression to Nursing, Health and Social Care*. Each allied health profession has its own entry requirements and path to qualification. It is possible to enter most of these professions at different levels. For example, if you don't have A levels, but do have four or five good GCSEs, you could join in a support or therapy assistant role.

See **www.nhscareers.nhs.uk**.

HEALTHCARE SCIENTISTS

Biomedical scientists carry out lab tests to support doctors in diagnosing and treating disease. The majority specialise in a particular area, such as pharmacy or histopathology (the analysis of tissue samples from surgical ops).

You can become a biomedical scientist through a number of routes:

- take a degree in biomedical science
- take a degree in another science, then take a 'top-up' course
- go in after A levels, in which case you'll still have to take a biomedical degree on day release but may be sponsored by your employer.

It's also possible, and in many cases preferable, to move into research and lab work after you've qualified with a medical degree. In fact, some fields are closed to non-medical graduates. Check with the Institute of Biomedical Science, **www.ibms.org**.

Pharmacists (in hospitals or in the community) make up prescriptions, monitor dosages and advise on use of medication. The route to becoming a pharmacist is more straightforward (see page 68) – you've got to do a four-year Master of Pharmacy degree followed by one year of training based in a pharmacy practice.

See Royal Pharmaceutical Society of Great Britain **www.rpharms.com**.

DENTAL HYGIENIST AND DENTAL THERAPIST

A dental hygienist works to prevent dental problems from arising by performing routine hygiene including scaling and polishing teeth, applying sealants and advising on oral hygiene. You'll need two A levels and the General Dental Council's Diploma in Dental Hygiene.

See British Society of Dental Hygiene & Therapy **www.bsdht.org.uk**.

Dental therapists can do all of the above and more – including taking dental impressions, dental radiography, placing preformed crowns and even doing extractions under certain conditions. You'll need two A levels and a Diploma in Dental Therapy (which takes 27 months).

See British Association of Dental Therapists **www.badt.org.uk**.

DENTAL TECHNICIAN

This is the unseen and unsung hero or heroine of the dental world, who sits in a lab making the dentures, crowns, veneers, bridges and dental braces on which the dentist and the patient rely. Your 'customers' are the dentists, and you'll work to their orders and prescriptions, using a range of materials, for example gold, porcelain and plastic, to design and build appliances to meet each patient's need. The entry requirement is a BTEC National Diploma in Dental Technology, for which A levels are more than enough for entry.

See Dental Technologists Association **www.dta-uk.org**.

MEDICAL JOURNALISM

This is a very fast-growing field, and an option for those who decide they'd rather observe their profession and use their medical knowledge to educate the wider public, some of whom may be confused by medical jargon and processes. Some universities now offer degrees in medical journalism, in some cases open only to medical undergraduates who have completed their pre-clinical years.

See Medical Journalists' Association
www.mjauk.org.

Professional bodies

Professional bodies are responsible for overseeing a particular profession or career area, ensuring that people who work in the area are fully trained and meet ethical guidelines. Professional bodies may be known as institutions, societies and associations. They generally have regulatory roles: they make sure that members of the profession are able to work successfully in their jobs without endangering lives or abusing their position.

Professional bodies are often involved in training and career development, so courses and workplace training may have to follow the body's guidelines. In order to be fully qualified and licensed to work in your profession of choice, you will have to follow the professional training route. In many areas of work, completion of the professional training results in gaining chartered status – and the addition of some extra letters after your name. Other institutions may award other types of certification once certain criteria have been met. Chartered or certified members will usually need to take further courses and training to ensure their skills are kept up to date.

What professional bodies are there?
Not all career areas have professional bodies. Those jobs that require extensive learning and training are likely to have bodies with a regulatory focus. This includes careers such as engineering, law, construction, health and finance. If you want to work in one of these areas, it's important to make sure your degree course is accredited by the professional body – otherwise you may have to undertake further study or training later on.

Other bodies may play more of a supportive role, looking after the interests of people who work in the sector. This includes journalism, management and arts-based careers. Professional bodies may also be learned bodies, providing opportunities for further learning and promoting the development of knowledge in the field.

Can I join as a student?
Many professional bodies offer student membership – sometimes for free or for reduced fees. Membership can be extremely valuable as a source of advice, information and resources. You'll have the opportunity to meet other students in the field, as well as experienced

professionals. It will also look good on your CV, when you come to apply for jobs.

See below for a list of professional bodies in medicine, dentistry and optometry.

MEDICINE
British Medical Association
www.bma.org.uk

Royal College of Obstetricians and Gynaecologists
www.rcog.org.uk

Royal College of Psychiatrists
www.rcpsych.ac.uk

The Royal College of Radiologists
www.rcr.ac.uk

The Royal College of Surgeons of England
www.rcseng.ac.uk

The Royal College of Surgeons of Edinburgh
www.rcsed.ac.uk

The College of Emergency Medicine
www.collemergencymed.ac.uk

DENTISTRY
British Dental Association
www.bda.org

General Dental Council
www.gdc-uk.org

Faculty of Dental Surgery
www.rcseng.ac.uk/fds

Faculty of General Dental Practice
www.fgdp.org.uk

British Orthodontic Society
www.bos.org.uk

British Society of Periodontology
www.bsperio.org.uk

British Endodontic Society
www.britishendodonticsociety.org.uk

Association of Consultants and Specialists in Restorative Dentistry
www.restdent.org.uk

British Association of Oral and Maxillofacial Surgeons
www.baoms.org.uk

British Association of Oral Surgeons
www.baos.org.uk

OPHTHALMICS
The Royal College of Ophthalmologists
www.rcophth.ac.uk

General Optical Council
www.optical.org/

College of Optometrists
www.college-optometrists.org

Institute of Optometry
www.ioo.org.uk

British and Irish Orthoptic Society
www.orthoptics.org.uk

PHARMACY
Royal Pharmaceutical Society of Great Britain
www.rpharms.com

British Pharmacological Society
www.bps.ac.uk

Graduate destinations

Medicine and dentistry
HESA Destination of Leavers of Higher Education

Each year, comprehensive statistics are collected on what graduates are doing six months after they complete their course. The survey is co-ordinated by the Higher Education Statistics Agency (HESA) and provides information about how many graduates move into employment (and what type of career) or further study and how many are believed to be unemployed.

The full results across all subject areas are published by the Higher Education Careers Service Unit (HECSU) and the Association of Graduate Careers Advisory Services (AGCAS) in *What Do Graduates Do?*, which is available from **www.ucasbooks.com**.

	Medicine and dentistry
In UK employment	78.0%
In overseas employment	0.5%
Working and studying	6.7%
Studying in the UK for a higher degree	3.9%
Studying in the UK for a teaching qualification	0.4%
Undertaking other further study or training in the UK	4.6%
Studying overseas	0.1%
Not available for employment, study or training	1.1%
Assumed to be unemployed	2.5%
Other	2.3%

Marketing, Sales and Advertising Professionals	0.3%
Commercial, Industrial and Public Sector Managers	0.8%
Scientific Research, Analysis & Development Professionals	1.3%
Engineering Professionals	0.1%
Health Professionals and Associate Professionals	89.6%
Education Professionals	0.2%
Business and Financial Professionals and Associate Professionals	0.4%
Information Technology Professionals	0.1%
Art, Design, Culture and Sports Professionals	0.5%
Legal Professionals	0.0%
Social & Welfare Professionals	0.3%
Other Professionals, Associate Professional and Technical Occupations	0.9%
Numerical Clerks and Cashiers	0.1%
Other Clerical and Secretarial Occupations	0.9%
Retail, Catering, Waiting and Bar Staff	2.3%
Other Occupations	2.2%
Unknown Occupations	0.0%

Owing to rounding, total might not equal 100%

Reproduced with the kind permission of HECSU/AGCAS What Do Graduates Do? 2010.
All data comes from the HESA Destinations of Leavers from Higher Education Survey 2008/09.

Unistats®

from universities and colleges in the UK

Which university is right for you?

Compare by:
- Student satisfaction
- Job prospects
- UCAS points

HIGHER EDUCATION FUNDING COUNCIL FOR ENGLAND

UCAS

Visit www.direct.gov.uk/unist
The official university comparison

Entry routes

ProgressionSeries

Routes to qualification

MEDICINE

In essence, qualifying as a hospital doctor or GP will involve three main stages:

1 medical degree
2 generalist training, known as the foundation programme
3 specialist training, including specialist exams.

The undergraduate medical degree lasts five years. It provides an introduction to the theory of the medical sciences and to practical clinical duties. It covers the entire range of medical specialisms in brief.

The foundation programme is the training framework for postgraduate medical education in the UK. The first year of post-medical school training is now known as F1, and the second year as F2. For new medical graduates, the foundation programme aims to offer a coherent, managed programme of learning integrated into trainees' first introduction into working in the NHS. A commitment to improved career planning for doctors early in their careers means that you will have a better understanding of the breadth of career opportunities in the NHS, access to good information about future workforce trends in clinical specialities and – most importantly – the opportunity to think about and discuss your own attributes and aspirations and align these to the likelihood of success.

Once you have completed the foundation programme, you can progress to training either as a GP or in a specialism of your choice. This will take three to six years.

In 2008, a locally led, staggered recruitment for speciality training in England was introduced, without a national IT system for applications. For further details, see **www.mmc.nhs.uk**.

The chart opposite outlines the main stages, and how long they will take.

FROM MEDICAL STUDENT TO SENIOR HOSPITAL DOCTOR

1 MEDICAL DEGREE

Five years

Covers basic medical sciences and practical clinical activities, and gives students exposure to the different specialities within medicine.

2A F1 TRAINEE

One year

The first year of Foundation Programme training, involving basic in-hospital training under supervision. F1 training will typically involve three four-month placements, including general medicine and general surgery. There will also be formal teaching and you will have a supervisor. You should be allocated an F1 posting by your medical school. Successful completion of the F1 year will result in full registration with the General Medical Council (GMC).

2B F2 TRAINEE

One year

This is made up of a further three four-month placements, possibly one of which will be in a speciality that has a shortage of doctors. There will also be formal teaching and a supervised audit project. During this year, you'll also apply to compete for a place on a training programme as a speciality registrar, working towards a post as a hospital consultant, or as a GP registrar, training to become a GP.

9–15 years total

3 SPECIALIST TRAINING (RUN-THROUGH TRAINING)

- Approximately five to six years
- You will now move into a specialist field
- Hospital training will typically lead to a certificate of specialist training and consultant status.

3 GENERAL PRACTICE TRAINING (RUN-THROUGH TRAINING)

- Approximately three years
- This part of your training will probably be community-based and you'll still have to sit the general practice specialism exams.

CERTIFICATE OF COMPLETION OF TRAINING (CCT)

CONSULTANT

GP PRINCIPAL

Qualifying will take longer if:

- **you take an intercalated course** – ie an undergraduate course sandwiched around another year's (or two years') study of a related subject: for example biomedicine or microbiology. If you're interested in this option, you should ask the medical schools if it is offered before you apply
- **you have to take a pre-med course** – if you don't have the necessary science A levels, you can take a 30-week pre-med course to bring you up to A-level standard
- **you work flexibly while completing your training** – ie you work part time or job share or take a career break part-way through.

QUALIFYING IN NORTHERN IRELAND AND SCOTLAND

Entry requirements, course content and career paths are the same all across the UK. Scottish Highers are acceptable at medical and dental schools throughout the UK: mostly A and B grades will be preferred.

DENTISTRY

Qualifying as a General Dental Practitioner involves two main stages:

1 dental degree
2 one year's professional vocational training (VT) in general practice.

Qualifying as a hospital dental specialist takes longer, but also requires two stages:

1 dental degree
2 several years' specialist in-hospital training, including specialist exams.

Qualifying as a dental surgeon (ie oral or maxillofacial) takes longer again, and requires three stages:

1 dental degree
2 several years' specialist in-hospital training, including specialist exams
3 the small matter of a medical degree, which you'll probably take while training.

The following diagram shows the key qualification stages:

FROM DENTAL STUDENT TO GENERAL PRACTITIONER OR DENTAL SURGEON

1 DENTAL DEGREE

Five years

Covers basic medical sciences, anatomy, pathology, physiology and practical clinical activities, plus dental science materials.

6–15+ years total

For general dental practitioners

For non-surgical hospital-based specialisms

For dental surgery specialism

2 VOCATIONAL DENTAL PRACTITIONER

One year

This training usually involves working under supervision on your own patient list in a general dental practice.

2 F1 OR F2 TRAINEE

Approximately two years

You'll join the 'Foundation' medical training route and start to gain general experience of a range of hospital specialities, before you can start to focus on your preferred dental speciality.

2A F1 OR F2 TRAINEE

Approximately two years – see left.

2B MEDICAL DEGREE

Approximately four years, concurrently with F1 and F2 training. Those wishing to become dental surgeons will have to qualify in medicine either before or during their specialist hospital training.

GENERAL DENTAL PRACTITIONER

At first you'll probably work as an 'associate' practitioner in someone else's practice, and will pay part of the fees you earn to the practice owner in return for use of the surgery, equipment and staff. Later on, you may become a practice owner (principal).

SPECIALIST TRAINING

Approximately five years

You'll now be working in one or two dental specialisms. By the end of this stage you should have completed the exams for the specialism you've chosen.

SPECIALIST TRAINING

See left.

DENTAL SPECIALIST

For example, orthodontist, periodontist, oral surgeon.

DENTAL SURGERY SPECIALIST

For example, maxillofacial surgeon.

Want to see UCAS in action?
Visit www.ucas.tv to watch

video diaries

case studies

how-to guides

UCAS

Introducing
pharmacy

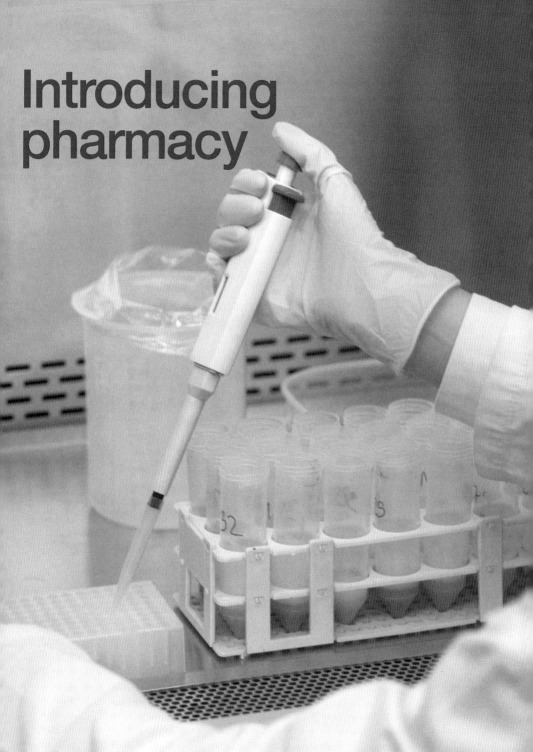

Progression**Series**

It could be you...

... dispensing and providing advice on prescriptions

... advising on patients' medical treatments

... developing gene therapy

... ensuring resources for medicines are well spent

... enabling the best welfare for animals

– community pharmacist

– hospital pharmacist

– industrial pharmacist

– primary care pharmacist

– veterinary pharmacist

... and lots more besides. Could a degree in pharmacy be for you? The aim of this section is to help you decide.

Why pharmacy?

Pharmacists are experts in medicines and pharmacy is one of the fastest growing areas of healthcare. According to the Association of the British Pharmaceutical Industry (ABPI), the pharmaceutical industry invested £4.4 billion in UK research and development (R&D) in 2009 and employs over 72,000 people, including 27,000 scientists and doctors. The pharmaceutical industry makes a major contribution to the British economy as well as developing new medicines to treat diseases all over the world.

A fifth of the UK's population has some sort of chronic or long-term illness and, over the next 50 years or so, huge developments in science will necessitate the introduction of new medicines to treat all types of illnesses and diseases. Pharmacists will play an important role at each stage of their evolution, from conception through to distribution and treatment.

In this section, we will look at the kinds of careers on offer in pharmacy. Read on to find out about what they involve, the working environment, typical salaries, career prospects and training requirements.

What do pharmacists do?

Pharmacy is all about designing, evaluating, producing and using medicines, and is based on a mixture of the chemical, biological and medical sciences. Since pharmacists are thoroughly trained in all aspects of pharmacy they are rightly considered to be experts in medicines, knowing how drugs can affect the body, the kind of side effects they can cause and how they can interact with other substances. Pharmacists use their knowledge to advise a range of people – from doctors and other medical professionals to patients and their families – on the correct dosage and combination of drugs. Pharmacists are often a person's first port of call when requiring help with a health issue and can and will refer them on to their doctor where necessary.

Pharmacists normally specialise in one of the following main fields:
- hospital
- community/retail
- industrial
- primary care
- regulatory
- academic
- armed forces
- veterinary.

Information on each of these areas can be found over the next few pages, followed by a look at the skills you will need to enjoy a career in pharmacy, the pay and opportunities offered and the various routes to qualification.

HOSPITAL PHARMACIST

Hospital pharmacists – as you may have guessed from the job title – work in hospitals. They work within a hospital's own pharmacy service and normally within the NHS, although some are employed by the private sector.

Hospital pharmacists are responsible for the safe, correct and most cost-effective use of medicines, and use the specialist knowledge they have gained during their degree and afterwards to advise both patients and doctors on the most appropriate drugs to take and at what dose. They also consult with other healthcare professionals to ensure that their patients are receiving the most relevant and effective medicines for their condition. Occasionally hospital pharmacists will also advise on the production of drugs and other medicinal treatments.

Typical duties include:

- taking patients' drug histories on ward rounds to help doctors decide on the most effective course of treatment. This can include advising on the side effects of one drug, particularly when it is combined with another, and how suitable certain drugs can be when taking into consideration a patient's particular health issues
- working alongside doctors, nurses and other healthcare professionals to ensure that they are giving patients a safe, cost-effective and relevant treatment programme
- talking to patients about possible side effects and interactions of the drugs that they take. This is especially important for patients who may have to take several drugs concurrently
- monitoring a treatment programme and adjusting dosages or drugs if necessary
- logging and reporting side effects to drug manufacturers
- advising a patient's relatives about their treatment, and liaising with their community pharmacist and GP
- preparing medicines and ensuring that they are kept under optimum and sterile conditions
- making sure that a patient's medication reaches them in the correct form and dose; this could be tablets, capsules, creams, inhalers, etc
- supervising less qualified or less experienced staff in their work
- making sure they keep up to date with research and development in the pharmaceutical industry so they are aware of new drugs on the market
- writing drug use guidelines for their hospital
- working with individual wards on their budgets and spending
- establishing clinical trials and seeing if a pharmaceutical company's claim about a drug stands up to rigorous testing.

Hospital pharmacists with a bit more experience often take on teaching duties, both in university pharmacy departments and within their hospital. In the latter case, they could lecture clinical staff on different drug treatment aspects.

COMMUNITY PHARMACISTS

The main job of a community pharmacist is to dispense and sell medicines and other related products to the general public and other medical colleagues. Normally they manage a shop and will make up prescriptions for customers and advise on their dosage. They are also often the first port of call for queries about the management of minor illnesses and their symptoms, often by supplying over-the-counter (OTC) medicines.

The majority of medicines are supplied ready-made by manufacturers but occasionally they need to be made up in the pharmacy, especially if a different strength is required. Some chemists also offer specialist healthcare services such as blood pressure monitoring and screening for diabetes. Community pharmacists use computers to check on stock control, produce labels for prescriptions and to keep health and medicine records on their customers.

As opposed to other pharmacy fields, community pharmacists also need to understand retail management since they often run their own shops. They must be able to supervise and train their staff so that they give a good service to their customers, market their products effectively and keep records of stock and accounts.

INDUSTRIAL PHARMACISTS

Industrial pharmacists focus on discovering safe and effective new drugs, as well as looking at the overall development of new drugs, overseeing their manufacture and marketing the finished product. They also try to improve current medicines and find new ways of formulating old drugs. Industrial pharmacists often work alongside pharmacologists, chemists, microbiologists and experts within the pharmaceutical industry.

A popular area of work for industrial pharmacists is in medicine formulation: the process of turning a medicinal compound into a product that can be taken safely and effectively by patients. In order to do this, they must carefully check concentrations, impurity levels and the stability of the particular medicine. This is done during the production process, from clinical trials right through to the launch of a drug.

Another area of employment is in manufacturing and production, in which industrial pharmacists will set up and standardise the manufacturing processes for drugs

and medicines normally on a huge scale. Quality assurance needs the expertise of industrial pharmacists too. In this, they will examine the processes and raw materials needed to make a certain medicine and then analyse the final result. This includes determining a product's shelf life and stability.

Before drugs can be marketed, a licence must be obtained from the Department of Health, and industrial pharmacists can help with this by collating and presenting the data needed to support the application.

PRIMARY CARE PHARMACISTS

This career area has developed over the last five to ten years. The main responsibility of a primary care pharmacist is to develop lists of preferred, commonly prescribed drugs (known as formularies), to improve the way in which a practice spends money on prescribing to make it as cost-effective as possible, and to give pharmaceutical advice where needed in GP practices.

They may also run clinics for patients needing cholesterol or anti-coagulant monitoring and review the medication plan for people with complex drug prescription plans. While the number of pharmacists working in this area is quite small, it is gradually growing as an area in which to work.

REGULATORY PHARMACISTS

Regulatory pharmacists work for such government offices as the MHRA – the Medicines and Healthcare products Regulatory Agency, whose remit it is to protect public health. They make sure that the medicines proposed by drug companies are safe before they are manufactured so that they can be marketed to the general public confidently. Critical evaluation skills are essential in this specialism.

ACADEMIC PHARMACISTS

Academic pharmacists work in a variety of areas – teaching, researching, practising or a combination of the three. This makes for a stimulating career based primarily in universities, hospitals and research institutes. Teacher practitioners normally spend around 60% of their time working in a hospital, community or industrial pharmacy and the remainder as a lecturer in pharmacy. They also can be heavily involved in research, researching anything from drug design to the provision of pharmacy services. Since the work is so varied, a career in this area is bound to be interesting and rewarding as the work you do will help to improve people's lives.

ARMED FORCES PHARMACISTS

The Army Medical Services (AMS) is an essential part of the British Army and travels with them wherever they go. Pharmacists working within this area are often deployed at very short notice to anywhere in the world in order to support the armed forces during war, conflict or on peacekeeping missions. The AMS itself is made up of the Royal Army Medical Corps (RAMC), the Royal Army Veterinary Corps (RAVC), the Royal Army Dental Corps (RADC) and The Queen Alexandra's Royal Army Nursing Corps (QARANC). Pharmacists can work in the RAMC as pharmacist officers either after qualifying in a relevant degree or through sponsored training. They can also be taken on to support the Royal Navy (RN) or Royal Air Force (RAF).

A pharmacist working in this area is mainly responsible for distributing medical supplies to support current operations and overseas units. This includes medicines, dressings and medical equipment of all sorts. In field hospitals, they provide pharmacy support and advice to their commanding officer. Additionally they may be called upon to advise on such pharmaceutical matters as storage, distribution, security, and the prescription, distribution and supply of drugs. Since they are also taken on as commissioned officers, pharmacists in this area will be expected to undertake military duties as stipulated by their commanding officer.

VETERINARY PHARMACISTS

Pharmacists don't just deal with people; they also provide valuable support for the welfare of animals. Since autumn 2005, the government has placed a greater emphasis on involving pharmacists in the provision of animal medicines and the dispensing of veterinary prescriptions.

Over 50% of pharmacy customers have a pet and many don't know what to give their animals for common healthcare issues such as worms and fleas. Pharmacists also help farmers by dispensing medicines for farm livestock.

Veterinary pharmacists work in all branches of the profession, from giving advice to customers about the health of their pets – cats, dogs, rabbits and fish – to supplying medicine to livestock farmers for cattle, sheep, pigs or goats. This area in particular requires skills in selling and business so it could appeal to people with an entrepreneurial interest. This area can also lead you into teaching, industry or working for a government body such as the Veterinary Medicines Directorate.

WORKING ENVIRONMENT

There are as many different working environments for pharmacists as there are types of specialisms.

- **Hospital pharmacists** obviously work within a hospital setting primarily but will sometimes work in health centres, nursing homes, hospices and GP surgeries.
- **Community pharmacists** will be based in retail environments, such as chemists and supermarkets.
- **Industrial pharmacists** are most commonly employed by pharmaceutical companies to work on the development and testing of new drugs from conception to marketing.
- **Primary care pharmacists** normally work either for a GP practice or for the local health authority; in the latter case they will be allocated to practices in their area.
- **Regulatory pharmacists** work for government bodies such as the MHRA, in a lab and office setting.
- **Academic pharmacists** are based predominantly in universities, hospitals and research institutes.
- **Armed forces pharmacists** work wherever the Army or other armed forces need them both at home and abroad, in war, conflict and on peacekeeping missions.
- **Veterinary pharmacists** can be based either within a retail setting, helping to advise customers on common animal illnesses and medications or in rural settings working with the farming community.

Most vacancies for these jobs will be found in larger towns and cities, although community/retail pharmacists can do well in rural settings. Working hours tend to be fairly regular at around 39 hours a week. However, this may include evening and weekend work on a rota basis as people's healthcare problems happen at all times.

The career for you?

CAREER PROSPECTS

People and animals will always need medicine so career prospects for pharmacists are steady and positive. Opportunities for progression are good too, especially within structured organisations such as the NHS.

Salaries for pharmacists vary depending on experience, employer and specialism. Generally, they are likely range from £21,176 to £27,625 a year at the start of their career in the NHS, or slightly more if working for another employer – for example, in industry. Experienced pharmacists – for example a consultant or manager of pharmaceutical services – working in the NHS can earn up to £77,000.

Self-employed pharmacists, such as those working in retail pharmacy with some experience behind them, can earn between £27,000 to £36,000 a year depending on the size and success of their business. Experienced pharmacists can expect to earn over £52,500 a year.

WHAT SKILLS DO YOU NEED?

Many, if not most, of the skills below are applicable to all pharmacy disciplines.

- **Tact and discretion:** to deal with delicate or sensitive issues that can require consultation with GPs, for example
- **Interpersonal skills:** to deal compassionately and patiently with the general public and to motivate staff
- **Good management skills:** to run a shop, a lab or a research project efficiently and profitably
- **Analytical skills:** since many pharmacists work in labs or production/manufacturing environments, they have to use specialist equipment and automated systems. Therefore strong analytical skills are essential to operate these machines and systems and interpret the results
- **Communication and liaison skills:** to deal with all kinds of customers and regulatory bodies
- **Teamwork skills:** since research is mainly undertaken in teams; you'll need to like working closely with other people and sharing your knowledge.

Routes to qualification

A career in pharmacy is a scientific one, which will involve a high level of education and training. Registered pharmacists must get a degree in pharmacy from a university or school of pharmacy that has been approved by the Royal Pharmaceutical Society of Great Britain (**www.rpharms.com**). An undergraduate pharmacy course usually lasts for four years and you will normally need A levels in chemistry and two of biology/maths/physics. If you've got an A level in chemistry, one other science subject (preferably biology) and then another subject you may also be considered; contact your preferred universities to ask their admissions requirements on this. Scottish students normally need a strong emphasis on the sciences in their Highers and particularly in chemistry.

Once you have graduated, you'll then have to complete a pre-registration year of supervised work experience in a Royal Pharmaceutical Society approved organisation; often this can be split between two different fields, eg six months in industry and six months in a hospital or retail pharmacy. Once you have completed this year, you need to pass an entrance exam to join the society.

Since much of the work in industrial pharmacy is lengthy and expensive, pharmacists in this field must be happy to do further research in a relevant field. This could involve on-the-job training or research for a postgraduate degree in such areas as toxicology or pharmacology.

Pharmacy graduates interested in a career in scientific research and development may wish to carry on studying for an MSc or PhD in such areas as bio or chemical science before starting out on their career.

Pharmacologists

Pharmacologists are responsible for studying the effects of drugs on humans and animals, as well as researching and developing – through experiments – new drugs that can be used to treat disease. They also look at aspects of food processing and agricultural products.

To find out exactly how drugs work and the effects they have on humans, pharmacologists will work with such substances as food additives, cosmetics, medicines and drugs.

Pharmacologists based in pharmaceutical companies will work on drugs developed to help prevent or alleviate diseases such as cancer and Alzheimer's. They might test drugs on samples of tissues, organs and cells from either animals or from human volunteers. Those working in chemical companies often work with pesticides, detergents, food additives and solvents to ensure that products containing these ingredients are safe.

Graduates with a pharmacology degree cannot use this to practise as a pharmacist.

WORKING ENVIRONMENT

The major employers of pharmacologists are the pharmaceutical and chemical industries, which are mainly based in south east England. Other vacancies appear in universities, hospitals, research organisations and government departments.

Working hours are regular and typically clock in at 39 hours a week from Monday to Friday.

CAREER PROSPECTS

With ongoing growth in research and development in drugs and other products, there will always be a demand for pharmacologists. The salary they command depends on their employer, their role within the organisation and the responsibilities they have. Pharmacologists working in academia may start on a salary of around £23,000 (pre-doctoral) or £28,000 (post-doctoral). Senior level pharmacologists can command salaries of up to £100,000. Industry pays better than academia.

WHAT SKILLS DO YOU NEED?

Pharmacologists need:

- good analytical abilities
- accuracy
- a methodical approach to deal with experiments
- confidence and competence in dealing with technical equipment
- good written communication skills to be able to write clear and accessible reports
- good verbal communication skills to work effectively within teams.

ROUTES TO QUALIFICATION

Pharmacologists must have a degree from an approved university. Pharmacology can be studied either alone or together with another subject such as physiology, chemistry or immunology. If you fancy doing a degree in another science subject such as biochemistry, immunology or medicine chemistry, you can follow this up with a postgraduate pharmacology qualification. Research posts normally require an MSc or a PhD.

FURTHER INFORMATION

British Pharmacological Society **www.bps.ac.uk**
Association of the British Pharmaceutical Industry **www.abpi.org.uk**
The Royal Pharmaceutical Society of Great Britain **www.rpharms.com**
The National Pharmacy Association **www.npa.co.uk**
NHS Careers **www.nhscareers.nhs.uk**

Introducing toxicology

It could be you...

... assessing environmental hazards   – environmental toxicologists

... ensuring the food we eat is safe   – industrial toxicologists

... advising on how to treat cases of poisoning   – clinical toxicologists

... acting as an expert witness in trials   – forensic toxicologists

... and lots more besides. Could a degree in toxicology be for you? The aim of this section is to help you decide.

Why toxicology?

Toxicology enables us to identify, understand, monitor and evaluate the harmful effects of toxic materials, chemicals and radiation on humans and animals, as well as in the environment. This can include pesticides in the food we buy, air pollutants, water chemicals and toxins found in dump sites. It is described by the British Toxicology Society as 'the study of how harmful effects may occur in humans, other animals, plants and the environment, and how they can be avoided or minimised'.

In this section of the handbook, we will look at the kinds of careers on offer in toxicology. Read on to find out about what they involve, the working environment, typical salaries, career prospects and training requirements.

What do toxicologists do?

There are between 3,000 and 5,000 people employed as toxicologists in the UK, working in such organisations as the National Health Service and the Forensic Science Service, in industry and in consultancy. And just as there are many types of employers there is more than one type of toxicologist: in fact there are eight. These are in the following areas:

- industrial
- pharmaceutical
- academic
- clinical
- forensic
- regulatory
- occupational
- ecotoxicology.

Information on each of these areas can be found over the next few pages, followed by a look at the skills you will need to enjoy a career in toxicology, the pay and opportunities offered, and the various routes to qualification.

INDUSTRIAL TOXICOLOGISTS

Industrial toxicologists play an essential role in developing safe and effective products such as pharmaceuticals, petrochemicals, pesticides, cosmetics, food and drink, and household cleaning products. They look at the way chemicals might harm people, animals and plants, and try to find ways to avoid or reduce damage to the environment.

There are very strict controls in place to help protect production workers, consumers and the environment so all products must be carefully checked for toxicity. This happens both before and after manufacture to check that they have not been accidentally contaminated in any way during the process. How rigorously products are tested depend on what they will be used for and how much they will be used.

To discover how dangerous a chemical can be, toxicologists experiment on tissue and cell cultures, on animals and on human volunteers. Toxicologists working for pharmaceutical companies help to develop new drugs that can fight disease. They test how strong a drug is and if it carries any side effects. Those working for the food industry often test things like additives to ensure that they will not harm consumers – for example through causing cancer.

Occupational and industrial toxicologists help to advise people on their working conditions and advise people who handle chemicals, while other toxicologists in this field work in hospitals to treat patients suffering from drug poisoning by finding out what they took and how much they ingested.

PHARMACEUTICAL TOXICOLOGISTS

One in five people in the UK has a chronic or long-term illness, normally requiring medication. While a person on trial is automatically presumed innocent until proven guilty, a new drug must always be considered toxic until tests show otherwise. Before drugs can be sold or prescribed, they must be tested rigorously in a series of *in vivo* and *in vitro* lab experiments. The tests performed are governed by regulations provided by regulatory authorities such as the Department of Health. These will give the final go-ahead once the preliminary results are available and the risk posed to humans is understood.

To assess risks accurately, pharmaceutical toxicologists must evaluate and assess data in various ways. Typically they will liaise with scientists to decide which studies need to be carried out and when, and then design, manage and implement these studies.

Once tests are under way, pharmaceutical toxicologists will look at and interpret results – either on an ongoing basis or at the end of a trial. They must also ensure that their tests and analysis meet with the conditions stipulated by the appropriate regulatory bodies.

It's not all lab-based work. Reports need to be written on the progress of the tests and meetings attended with other team members and scientists. Telephone and e-mail communication also forms a considerable part of the job.

ACADEMIC TOXICOLOGISTS

A career in academia might not sound like the most vibrant option at first, but university toxicologists enjoy varied, exciting and stimulating work. They work primarily in a university, giving lectures or instructing in practicals, and it is this atmosphere of lively enquiry that can make the job so enjoyable. Students arrive to learn and leave to work every year, so certainly one of the most rewarding aspects of this job is taking someone who knows virtually nothing about toxicology and mentoring them through their degree years to successful graduation.

Academic toxicologists don't just spend their time in the lecture hall or tutorial classroom. They also work a lot in labs carrying out research in collaboration with industry, research councils and independent charities, which often provide the funding for their research. By publishing the results of their research, university toxicologists help to improve communication amongst their colleagues within and outside academia.

This in turn enables a quick and effective progression in the design of new materials such as pesticides or medicines.

University toxicologists must run well organised, well developed and well equipped labs to achieve success in their research. This can lead to their developing 'centres of excellence' in toxicology, which in turn can bring about meetings with other scientists both in the UK and abroad. These days, there are more and more links between academia and industry and the government. By working together, they can share information as industry research findings tend to be more applied in nature than academic ones. Such collaboration works to the advantage of everyone: mankind and the environment. Academic toxicologists can also serve on government advisory committees, providing independent advice and opinion on the safety of chemicals.

CLINICAL TOXICOLOGISTS

Clinical toxicologists are normally medicine graduates who have gained specific knowledge of the adverse effects of drugs and chemicals on humans and will have the necessary knowledge on how to treat any poisoning that the chemicals can cause. Most toxicologists in this field will work in hospitals, often liaising closely with university clinical pharmacology departments.

The following are examples of a clinical toxicologist's duties:

- treating patients who have been poisoned with a drug or other chemical
- providing information and advice to colleagues working with poisoned patients
- interpreting and applying the results of tests carried out on patients who have been poisoned

- collecting and analysing data on the side effects of prescription drugs
- teaching toxicology to undergraduates and graduates.

Clinical toxicologists also are asked to advise on how new chemicals can be hazardous to the environment or to people using them in their workplace. Therefore, they need to have undergone thorough clinical training in case there is a clinical, rather than a toxicological, explanation for unusual symptoms experienced in a clinical investigation.

FORENSIC TOXICOLOGISTS

Forensic toxicologists mostly become involved with the medico-legal issues surrounding drugs and poisons. Their main duties include establishing and explaining the circumstances of legal cases in which drugs or chemicals are suspected, from drink-driving incidents to fatal accidents, suicides or murders where poisoning, either by accident or on purpose, is suspected.

A forensic toxicologist will often be called upon to prove that a person has ingested drugs so they must be able to isolate, identify and quantify toxic substances. They normally do this through the use of modern analytical procedures such as immunoassays to detect the presence or identity of drugs, and chromatographic and spectrometric assays to measure very small quantities of drugs, often in small samples.

The courts often ask forensic toxicologists to give evidence as an expert witness in trials, in order to state what type of drug was used in a crime, the amount that was taken, at what time it was ingested and by which method. They can also give opinions on whether certain levels of a drug could cause a condition and whether a drug was taken as an accidental or deliberate overdose.

Providing information like this requires a great deal of analytical ability to assess the relationship between drug levels and the possible responses in humans. Forensic toxicologists also need to understand how a drug's metabolism can affect its concentrations and the subsequent effects. In addition, they need to take into account such issues as drug interactions, tolerance, how effects can vary according to a person's age and how each individual can react differently to a drug despite rigorous clinical testing.

Careers in this field are normally offered in such organisations as the Home Office's Forensic Science Service, in private forensic laboratories and in hospital forensic medicine departments.

ECOTOXICOLOGISTS

As the name suggest, ecotoxicologists study the toxic effects of chemicals on the environment, a relatively new field within this career area. While they look at the immediate effect of individual organisms, their primary objective is seeing how these toxins can affect populations and ecosystems as a whole.

For an ecotoxicologist, the sub-lethal effects of toxins (such as changes in behaviour or reproduction in organisms) are more important than lethal effects as they have more far-reaching implications. An ecotoxicologist's duties include:

- monitoring the movement of pollutants through organisms in land-based and water-based food chains
- observing the metabolism and accumulation of pollutants in food chains
- identifying population changes after they have been affected by pollutants
- examining genetic changes, including an insect's

resistance to pesticides
- assessing how organisms react physiologically and biochemically when exposed to pollutants
- carrying out detailed ecological and toxicological studies on organisms that have been exposed to pollution in rivers and other water environments.

These duties normally involve ecotoxicologists designing models to predict how ecosystems will survive while affected by the presence of chemicals – but it can take a long time (often many years) to see the results of one's work. Ecosystems are complex and there can be variations in how each species responds to pollutants. To enable the most successful and accurate research, ecotoxicologists will work alongside field-based ecologists, sometimes for organisations and charities that strive to protect the environment, as well as colleagues in laboratories with the most up-to-date biochemical toxicology and chemistry techniques to hand.

REGULATORY TOXICOLOGISTS

Regulatory toxicologists normally work for the government and have the tricky task of answering questions about environmental hazards put to them by politicians and members of the general public. They also need to do this in a manner that is clear and easily understood by the layman.

Such questions could include demands about whether the test results on a new product really comply with the legal requirements, or whether factory workers might be at risk from chemicals they are exposed to at work – even if the data to date would suggest that they are not.

Sometimes, regulatory toxicologists do not have enough information to assess the hazards they have been asked about and cannot provide a clear solution to a problem. In these cases, they will have to fall back on their own knowledge of toxicological mechanisms and how these can be applied to different species, such as mankind.

If a clear assessment cannot be made, then a regulatory toxicologist will have to provide a prediction of the risk to the general public. This is where communication skills come to the fore, perhaps more so in this field of toxicology than in any other. A tactful approach and an empathic yet authoritative attitude is needed to reassure and educate the public.

OCCUPATIONAL TOXICOLOGISTS

Did you know that we are regularly exposed to chemicals in everyday products such as shampoos, soaps, foods and additives? These are also known as 'industrial chemicals' and occupational toxicologists are employed to look at the potential toxicity of such materials in the products in which they occur and in the resultant waste from their use.

Most of their time is spent analysing the effects of these chemicals on human health and ensuring that the people who produce them work in safe conditions and can handle them with confidence. This can extend to providing advice on treatment if someone has been adversely affected by a chemical or if this chemical has accidentally been released into a local area. Normally an occupational toxicologist would draw upon previous advice and experience on dealing with a similar situation in the past to form their suggestions on how to proceed.

Government regulations about the use of new chemicals will need someone to advise on how these might affect human health. Occupational toxicologists will therefore evaluate the already existing data to come to their conclusions and might also need to arrange new studies if more evidence and information is needed.

There are so many different chemicals that it is impossible for occupational toxicologists to be an expert on them all. Therefore they will focus on the regulatory and toxicity requirements of one type, but it is important that they are able to recognise the potential dangers of simultaneous exposure to more than one particular type of chemical.

The career for you?

WORKING ENVIRONMENT

Toxicologists work in a number of different environments, depending on their particular specialism. Some work for large companies, such as pharmaceuticals and water companies, who might employ several toxicologists in different fields, including genetics and reproductive toxins, pathology and clinical biochemistry. At the other end, a person might be the only toxicologist working in a very general role in a small company.

Contract research laboratories also take on industrial toxicologists to carry out toxicity studies on behalf of other companies, both large and small. This can be a great career choice as the labs perform studies in a wide variety of specialities and offer many different careers.

Industrial toxicologists also work with regulatory authorities to ensure that a company's products and processes comply with regulations on a local, national and international level. Examples of such employers include the Health and Safety Executive, the Medicines Control Agency and the Forensic Science Service.

Working hours tend to be quite regular, at around 35 to 39 hours per week, from Monday to Friday. However, you can expect to work odd shifts such as early starts, late finishes and weekend work, especially if you are working in a hospital or similar area.

CAREER PROSPECTS

Career prospects are generally good for all types of toxicologists as many companies need their skills in their production processes – and since the range of chemical products is ever increasing, opportunities for industrial toxicologists will keep on growing. Your skills will always be in demand!

As for pay, salaries vary according to the area in which you work. A typical starting range would be £22,000 to £25,000 a year. Some toxicologists earn in excess of £50,000 per year.

Opportunities for promotion are good, especially to more senior management positions, which generally means less lab time. While most toxicologists are employed, some work on a self-employed or freelance basis.

WHAT SKILLS DO YOU NEED?

The skills needed by all types of toxicologists are very similar and include the following:

- a methodical approach to your work
- an ability and desire to solve problems
- an analytical way of thinking
- numerical ability to deal with data
- a strong interest in science, the environment and public health and safety
- an understanding of the need for confidentiality, particularly in forensic toxicology
- an ability to work well in teams as well as on your own.

More generally, you will need to be aware of the debate surrounding using animals in medical and cosmetic research, for example, and be able to deal with criticism from members of the public who are against these forms of testing.

The ability to understand safety procedures and to handle toxic materials is essential as toxicologists often handle poisonous products. Computer skills are also important, as is a desire to keep informed of advances in technology.

Good communication skills – both verbal and written – are required as you'll often be writing reports and communicating with other scientists.

Routes to qualification

Toxicology can be studied at both undergraduate and postgraduate level. After the end of your A levels, you could opt for one of several degree courses in which toxicology is taught with a related subject such as biochemistry or pharmacology.

Your other option is to choose a degree in a related field, such as chemistry, biochemistry, pharmacology, pharmacy, medicine, veterinary medicine or environmental sciences. Once you have completed this study, you can then do a full- or part-time postgraduate course in which toxicology is taught on its own or combined with a subject such as forensic science or analytical chemistry. This would normally lead to an MSc qualification – master of science.

After qualification, if you wish, you could go on to study for a doctorate in the area – a PhD or a DPhil – which would involve research in a university department.

As a student or once you start working you can join the British Toxicology Society. This is a great way to keep up to date with what's happening in this area, as well as study for any further training and qualifications you might need.

After working in the field for several years, toxicologists can study for an advanced qualification in toxicology, such as the diploma of the Institute of Biology in toxicology. With a bit more experience they can apply for full membership of the British Toxicology Society.

FURTHER INFORMATION

The British Toxicology Society **www.thebts.org**
The Association of the British Pharmaceutical Industry **www.abpi.org.uk**
The Forensic Science Service **www.forensic.gov.uk**

Case studies

JUST WHAT DOES A CAREER IN MEDICINE,
DENTISTRY, OPTOMETRY AND RELATED FIELDS
OFFER YOU?

The following profiles show the wealth of exciting
opportunities that are yours for the taking.

Vocational dental practitioner

Arduthie Practice, Stonehaven

ANNA MAXWELL

Route into dentistry:
Scottish highers – mathematics, English, chemistry, physics, biology (2004); Advanced highers – mathematics, chemistry, biology (2005); BDS dentistry, University of Dundee (2010)

WHY DENTISTRY?

I am a people person, I like being part of a team, and I wanted to work in the caring professions. I was also good at science. I was an 'obvious candidate' for medicine, but it was too general for me. Dentistry gave me the opportunity to focus immediately and as it is a very patient-oriented profession, where good communication skills are vital, it seemed ideal.

HOW DID YOU GET WHERE YOU ARE TODAY?

I had already decided what I wanted to do before I went to university. My school arranged for me to shadow a local dentist when I was 14, which was very important in helping me decide on dentistry, as no one in my family was a dentist. The dentist who I worked with was tremendously helpful, providing advice during my course and when I was applying for my first job eight years later.

There are clear career paths for dentists after university. I applied for my current job during my last year and was appointed, subject to passing my Finals.

WHAT DOES YOUR JOB INVOLVE?

I work in a general dental practice within a team of 14 people, made up of dentists, nurses, hygienists, and receptionists. My general day is from 8am to 5pm, five days a week. Most of the time I treat patients, but I also spend time developing my skills. As I am a recent graduate, I spend some time each week learning from more experienced dentists.

In the future, I will be trying to get experience in the hospital and salaried services, as well as general practice, so that I have a broad range of experience.

WHAT HAS BEEN YOUR BIGGEST CHALLENGE?

There are lots of stresses and lots of support in dentistry. The trick is to use the support to reduce the stress! Students do not treat patients until they have completed many hours of learning and practice, including on phantom heads and on each other. However, treating your first patient (under supervision) is always a big moment. When I was a student I had an extremely anxious patient who had not been to the dentist for many years and who was very reluctant to be treated. The patient eventually relaxed and let me get to work, but it felt like a huge responsibility to make sure she did not feel a thing!

WHAT DO YOU LIKE MOST ABOUT YOUR JOB?

The best part of my job is the people – both the patients and my colleagues. It is uniquely satisfying to take away pain and to help someone to have a healthier mouth. My colleagues understand the pressures and pleasures of the job and are always ready to listen or give advice, be a shoulder to lean on, or have a laugh – whatever is needed.

ANNA'S TOP TIPS

Firstly, get as much work experience as you can before you apply to Dental School – in hospital and salaried services, as well as in different practices. This will help with your university applications and show you if dentistry is the right career for you. Secondly, make sure you do something completely unrelated to dentistry in your spare time. You will be a better dentist if you can relax sometimes and see your work in perspective. Also, the 'soft skills' employers want, such as teamwork experience, are often learnt outside the classroom.

Specialist registrar diabetes and endocrinology

Oxford Radcliffe Hospitals NHS Trust

HERMIONE PRICE

Route into medicine:

A levels – biology, chemistry, mathematics (1995); Intercalated BSc in pharmacology (1998), University of Leeds; MBChB medicine, University of Leeds (2001); DPhil medicine, University of Oxford (2010)

WHY MEDICINE?

I knew I wanted to be a doctor from the age of five, although there weren't any medical role models in my family, so I chose my GCSEs and A levels with a medical career in mind. I enjoy my profession because I have a genuine interest in science and in helping people, although I've come to realise that much as I'd like to, you can't help everyone.

HOW DID YOU GET WHERE YOU ARE TODAY?

My degree took six years instead of the usual five because I took an extra year to gain a BSc in pharmacology. The first two years of my degree were non-clinical, and the final three years were mainly practical, involving working in a wide variety of settings such as ward rounds, operating theatres, GP practices, children's wards, psychiatric hospitals and so on, as well as spending an elective in Fiji.

My interest in diabetes came about thanks to working with an inspirational endocrinologist while I was a medical student and a pre-registration house officer.

Once I had done my pre-registration year and completed my time as a senior house officer, I decided to specialise in endocrinology. I also chose to undertake a DPhil in a related area of research, focusing on how to motivate people to exercise more, both to satisfy my own interests and to enhance my career prospects. When I finish my specialist training next year I will be a consultant.

WHAT DOES YOUR JOB INVOLVE?

I look after people with diabetes and other hormone-related problems such as thyroid disease. I take various clinics each week: for example, antenatal clinics for pregnant women with diabetes on Monday mornings, where I work alongside an obstetrician; general endocrinology clinics on Monday afternoons and Wednesday mornings; and a diabetic clinic on Friday mornings. I also regularly work in general medicine; this could include seeing A&E emergencies or dealing with patients who are staying in hospital as part of a general medicine ward round.

My normal working days are from 9am to 5pm, but I work some longer days, from 9am to 10pm, night shifts 'on call', and one weekend in every eight 'on call'. Everyone has an important role in keeping the hospital functioning smoothly and I work alongside other doctors, nurses, physiotherapists, pharmacists, secretaries and many more.

WHAT HAS BEEN YOUR BIGGEST CHALLENGE?

As well as being a very enjoyable and rewarding career medicine is also strangely addictive! However, the long and antisocial hours mean that I have missed many Christmases, New Year's Eves, family parties, weddings, etc, and it's hard to maintain a normal family life. However, part-time working and flexible training are becoming increasingly available.

WHAT DO YOU LIKE MOST ABOUT YOUR JOB?

The job is highly varied and really exciting when you make a complex diagnosis and then provide a patient with treatment that improves their quality of life. Diabetes is a lifelong condition and I enjoy seeing the same patients over many years, through their ups and downs.

HERMIONE'S TOP TIPS

Try to gain relevant work experience in a hospital, GP surgery or nursing home. Biology A level is not compulsory but it will give you a head start when you get to medical school.

Optometrist

Specsavers

INA JAURRE

Route into optometry:
A levels – biology, chemistry, English, mathematics (2005); FD ophthalmic dispensing, City University (2007); BSc optometry, City University (2009)

WHY OPTOMETRY?

As a child I had always dreamt of being a lawyer. It's funny how a weekend job at an optometrist's changed my future. Although I was only doing clerical work, the health care profession intrigued me and it was definitely the start of my interest in the science of the eye. I was fascinated by the fact that a routine eye test could pick up various diseases or simply help someone pass their driving test or read a book more clearly.

Being a science enthusiast confirmed my decision. I declined my offers for law and reapplied just before my A level results through UCAS Extra. It's difficult to choose a degree and think 'Is that really what I want to do for the rest of my life?', but I added up the pros and cons and science was my way forward. Sometimes a little risk takes you down the right path, as long as you're positive.

HOW DID YOU GET WHERE YOU ARE TODAY?

I graduated from my foundation degree in dispensing with a distinction and moved into the second year of the BSc in optometry. On completing the degree I then carried out a pre-registration period to become a fully qualified optometrist. This entailed working full time under supervision while being continually assessed.

Moving into the working world was demanding and stressful as well as exciting – especially as I was still studying hard. It was without doubt the most difficult year of my studies, as well as the one in which I learnt the most, including getting to know the business side of optometry and putting the practical skills into practice in a real working environment. I found it was essential to find a good balance between working, studying and having a social life.

WHAT DOES YOUR JOB INVOLVE?

My day-to-day responsibilities include carrying out eye tests, and dispensing, adjusting and repairing glasses. I also control and replenish stock for essential items such as eye drops, leaflets and NHS forms. I work between three different stores in London. My hours are fairly basic: from 9.00am to 5.30pm. Every day I meet people from all sorts of backgrounds, age groups and ethnicities.

WHAT HAS BEEN YOUR BIGGEST CHALLENGE?

The biggest challenge I faced at work was my pre-registration period; trying to adjust to working full time while having to study alongside was not easy. My supervisor was not always around to help, but I was working with other optometrists who took the initiative to help me and tutor me when I needed. Had they all not been as supportive, I probably wouldn't have learnt as much as I did or passed my finals the first time round.

WHAT DO YOU LIKE MOST ABOUT YOUR JOB?

Being a practical person, optometry suits me perfectly. I have a profound interest in all the clinical and anatomical aspects of my career – including carrying out sight tests, dissecting an eye, and recording eye movements and muscle actions. Optometry is a career in which you never stop learning and helping other people, and I love that.

INA'S TOP TIPS

You need to be focused and be sure that you will enjoy the subject, as it's very specific. It makes it easier to learn and also easier to put the effort into studying. Taking time to relax and socialise is also vital.

Final year medical student

University of Warwick

MARTIN SLATTERY

Route into medicine:
A levels – biology, business studies, music (2002); AS mathematics (2001); BSc biological science, University of Salford (2006); MBChB Medicine, University of Warwick (graduating 2011)

WHY MEDICINE?

I was attracted to medicine because I thought it would be more interesting than working in a lab doing research. Also, the economic climate and job market at the time made me think that it would be more secure and would offer a better salary than other scientific jobs.

HOW DID YOU GET TO WHERE YOU ARE TODAY?

I based my A level choices on what I enjoyed and what I thought I was good at. Biology was my strongest subject so I pursued that at university, still with no clear idea of where I was heading.

In my final year I applied for various finance graduate training programmes, but my heart wasn't in it and, subsequently, I was not successful. I considered my options and that is when the idea of medicine dawned on me. It was a daunting prospect considering the competition for places at medical school, coupled with the length of training, but I have never regretted making that decision.

WHAT DOES YOUR MEDICAL TRAINING CONSIST OF?

My four-year course is split into two phases. Phase 1 is predominantly lecture based and lasts 18 months. Half a day each week is spent in the hospital receiving teaching from a consultant. If you pass the phase 1 exams you progress into phase 2, which is based in a clinical setting. You complete 12 eight-week rotations through different specialties including medicine, surgery, general practice, psychiatry, obstetrics, gynaecology and paediatrics.

Halfway through phase 2 you spend eight weeks on an elective – doing anything related to medicine anywhere in the world. I did general medicine at two hospitals in Borneo. One was in a developed city and another was in a rural setting which took 14 hours to get to by boat. It was a fantastic experience and I learnt a lot about healthcare abroad and my own strengths and weaknesses.

WHAT HAS BEEN YOUR BIGGEST CHALLENGE?

My forthcoming final exams are definitely the hardest part of the course. We will be assessed on the whole curriculum through both written and practical exams.

Medicine is a tough course and really tests your commitment to becoming a doctor. Also, the financial and time commitments are enormous and many people struggle to cope with these aspects of the training.

WHAT HAVE YOU ENJOYED MOST DURING YOUR TRAINING?

The best bits have been the elective and helping patients. It is very rewarding when you diagnose someone correctly for the first time or make someone feel better by spending time talking to them about their problems. As a doctor, people look up to you for help and advice when they are at their most vulnerable. This is a huge responsibility, but it also means that you can make a real difference to their lives.

WHAT'S NEXT?

After my final exams, I have a job lined up locally doing rotations in general medicine and general surgery. Once I have completed the two-year foundation programme, I will then decide on my specialism.

MARTIN'S TOP TIPS

Do not make the decision lightly: really think about it and don't be pushed into it. Get some work experience in a medical setting and try to get an idea of what doctors do in hospital. Don't give up: if you really want to do it, persevere.

Junior doctor (foundation year 2)

Oxford Radcliffe Hospitals NHS Trust

REBECCA SHAKIR

Route into medicine:

A levels – biology, chemistry, geology, geography, general studies, French AS (2003); Intercalated BSc medical sciences with immunobiology and pathology, Imperial College London (2007); MBBS medicine, Imperial College London (2009)

WHY MEDICINE?

A medical career combines my interest in science with the ability to care for people. You make a difference to your patients and their families, and have an impact on how they cope with their disease. Every day is unpredictable, each case is different, and there are many career paths to follow.

HOW DID YOU GET WHERE YOU ARE TODAY?

Since medicine is a vocational degree, becoming a doctor was a natural step. I enjoyed immunology in my pre-clinical years, and chose to do it as an intercalated BSc degree as part of my course. In my final year, I applied for a Foundation post in the Oxford deanery and was offered a Year 1 post at Wexham Park Hospital. I am now in my Foundation Year 2, doing trauma surgery at the John Radcliffe Hospital, Oxford. Foundation Year posts provide experience in different areas of medicine and surgery; I have worked in:

general surgery, infectious diseases, rheumatology, palliative medicine, and neurosurgery.

I am currently applying to Core Medical Training, the next step in training to become a physician, and am considering specialising in rheumatology, which applies the science of immunology to caring for patients with complex diseases.

WHAT DOES YOUR JOB INVOLVE?

Together with my registrar I am responsible for the day-to-day care of trauma patients on the ward. I prepare patients for surgery, then diagnose and manage any post-operative complications that may occur. I work with many different people: nurses, radiographers, radiologists, physiotherapists, occupational therapists, trauma technicians, trauma and A&E doctors, anaesthetists, and theatre staff.

My day on the Trauma Unit starts with a handover meeting at 8am, where we discuss the patients who have been admitted or operated on in the last 24 hours. I do a ward round with the ward registrar before organising x-rays, blood tests and other investigations. I am scheduled to finish at 4pm, but if there are patients who are unwell I often leave later.

As part of my rota, I spend days on call, where I am responsible for assessing and admitting new patients with the on-call registrar. These shifts finish after the evening ward round, usually at 10 or 10.30pm. I also do night shifts from 9pm to 9am. We also have days when we are based in theatre observing and assisting with operations.

WHAT HAS BEEN YOUR BIGGEST CHALLENGE?

When I started working as a doctor I found it difficult to adjust to situations where patients did not get better despite all my best efforts. However, I have worked in fantastic teams and always had support from my senior colleagues.

WHAT DO YOU LIKE MOST ABOUT YOUR JOB?

Despite its challenges, medicine is an incredibly gratifying career. I enjoy getting to know my patients and their families and being able to make a difference. Hearing 'thank you' from a patient as they leave hospital always puts a smile on my face. Because every day is different it is always challenging and interesting. It is great working closely in a team.

REBECCA'S TOP TIPS

Check out the different university courses as they differ in their teaching methods and choose the location of your university carefully – you will be there for five or six years! Do work experience and volunteering to make sure you will enjoy the job and get involved in medical school life – hobbies help you manage the pressure of work.

What others say...

These are extracts from case studies in previous editions of this book. They give some insights into the experiences and thoughts of people who were once in the same position as you.

Anand Mistry, general dental practitioner, finds dentistry fulfils his interest in science as well as his need for autonomy and variety.

He says, 'Dentistry is great because I enjoy the interaction with patients. I especially like treating children as they are full of surprises and you never quite know what to expect from them. Dentistry also allows time for many hobbies. Mine include scuba diving and travelling. However, you may find yourself giving dental advice to people in the strangest locations!'

Chris Hebbes, FY2 doctor and academic clinical demonstrator, says it is important to 'be flexible. I've been lucky in many ways but some of the 'luck' probably wouldn't have happened if I hadn't been adaptable and taken the opportunities available to me. Medicine is fun, challenging and has taken me to places that I couldn't have predicted.'

Leigh Bissett had studied law and worked abroad in Rwanda and Tanzania before turning to medicine. He says, 'I wanted a job that would stimulate my mind, as well as allow me to establish close relationships with the people I work and care for. I love the idea of being able to witness the outcomes of my work and feeling at the end of each day that I have done some good.'

'The hours are long and the overtime is unpaid. The upside is that you get to meet lots of people and get emotional rewards for the good work you do. Few jobs can boast such diversity – It's great not knowing what you are going to see in work today: emergencies, social problems that need to be resolved, and a whole lot more.'

Paul Zenn, a third year medical student, thinks back to the earliest stages of implementing his career choice: 'Applying to study medicine was daunting at first, especially when I heard all those statistics about the number of places on offer. When I got to the interviews I adopted an approach that all I could do was talk about who I am, what I believe in and my experiences, and hope they liked what they heard. Accordingly, my interviews were actually an extremely positive and enjoyable experience.'

Rebekah Stevens studied BSc Optometry and is now a pre-registration optometrist, which she says 'combines my love of biology with some physics – it is amazing to use mathematics to enable someone to see better!' Clearly her interest is in seeking out the unexpected: 'It is fantastic to help someone's health by finding a condition that they might not have noticed themselves and which might have gone untreated for some time.' Rebekah's top tip goes to the heart of the matter. 'Quiz ophthalmologists when you have the chance – they have a vast amount of experience to tap into!'

David Masson is a higher scientific officer in the Toxicology Unit of the Food Standards Agency. He says, 'I chose to work for the government because it gives me the feeling that all my skills as a toxicologist are being used to make our food safer to eat.' David's reminder for applicants is: 'communication is important! It's no use doing really complicated science if you can't explain it in simple terms to non-scientists. You'll need to convince people that they need to take action on your advice, eg a journalist, or a politician in charge of public health policy.'

Tom Vale suffered a serious illness at fourteen and spent a long time in hospital. While there he 'enjoyed the hospital atmosphere and doing some research into the initial diagnosis that was made of my condition really captured my imagination.'

He is now a FY2 student and says the hours are challenging but again, stress has its compensations. 'Working on-call in the evenings, overnight and at weekends can be horrendous – there are nowhere near as many staff out of hours and consequently my job is much busier. However, that's when most of my learning happens and sometimes seeing a seriously unwell patient can be extremely exciting!'

Kate Grant is a GP and found her training incredibly wide-ranging. 'I did rotations in every area of medicine that you can go into, including three in greater depth: complementary medicine, medical law and neonatal medicine. In my fourth year I did an elective in St Lucia and Dominica.'

Kate finds the human element of medicine both challenging and stimulating: 'The most challenging aspect is dealing with uncertainty. Of the 100 people who come in with a headache only one will have a brain tumour. It can be a stressful job at times, whether it's working out what a patient's real concerns are or dealing with patients who are aggressive or have impossibly high expectations. Communication skills are extremely important, especially as you have only a short space of time to see each patient.'

Sophie Vickers, now seven months into her career as an orthoptist, studied optics during her A level physics course and found the subject fascinating, especially since she had needed the services of an orthoptist in childhood which she sensed would make it easy for her to relate to patients. 'I like the fact that I can help people feel more comfortable, make my own mark and specialise in the subjects I most enjoy. I really like seeing children as I have to adapt my testing techniques and communication to get the most accurate testing and results.'

In such an evidence-based profession, Sophie explains, 'continuous learning is important – the profession is expanding and providing orthoptists with new and stimulating roles, so it offers good career prospects.'

Miriam Orcutt is unusual as a medical student in not having felt an early pull to science and health – she studied classical dance until the age of 16, but then something changed and she realised, 'that I wanted to do something where I could make a difference, which would challenge me daily and through which I could really interact with people. Subsequent experiences – volunteering in a local hospice and working as a healthcare assistant at hospitals – confirmed my initial thoughts.'

'Medicine becomes more a way of life than a job or a course. Bear in mind that studying medicine is a tough option: you work harder than on many other degrees and the amount of material covered is huge. If you are thinking about taking the plunge, ensure that you do a lot of work experience and talk to medical students before you apply. If you then decide you want to be a doctor, go for it! It is a very fulfilling career.'

Applicant
journey

Progression Series

SIX EASY STEPS TO UNIVERSITY AND COLLEGE

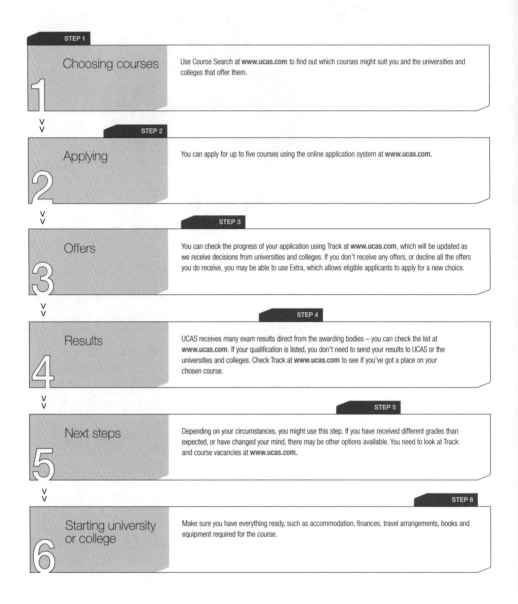

STEP 1

Choosing courses

Use Course Search at **www.ucas.com** to find out which courses might suit you and the universities and colleges that offer them.

STEP 2

Applying

You can apply for up to five courses using the online application system at **www.ucas.com**.

STEP 3

Offers

You can check the progress of your application using Track at **www.ucas.com**, which will be updated as we receive decisions from universities and colleges. If you don't receive any offers, or decline all the offers you do receive, you may be able to use Extra, which allows eligible applicants to apply for a new choice.

STEP 4

Results

UCAS receives many exam results direct from the awarding bodies – you can check the list at **www.ucas.com**. If your qualification is listed, you don't need to send your results to UCAS or the universities and colleges. Check Track at **www.ucas.com** to see if you've got a place on your chosen course.

STEP 5

Next steps

Depending on your circumstances, you might use this step. If you have received different grades than expected, or have changed your mind, there may be other options available. You need to look at Track and course vacancies at **www.ucas.com**.

STEP 6

Starting university or college

Make sure you have everything ready, such as accommodation, finances, travel arrangements, books and equipment required for the course.

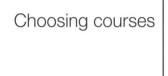

Choosing courses

1

Step 1 – Planning your application for medicine and dentistry

ENTRY REQUIREMENTS

Which subjects?
Contrary to popular belief, you no longer have to have all three sciences at A level to get into medical school. What's more, chemistry, not biology, is the most important subject at A level for entry to most medical schools.

However, the jury's still out on the need for biology at A level as well. Critics claim that students who don't have biology A level are at a disadvantage in the first year of medical school, which is highly science-based. But once students enter the more clinical (ie practical) side of the course, the gap is closed.

PLEASE NOTE:

This section covers routes into medicine and dentistry from A levels.

WHICH GRADES?

Competition for places in UK medical schools is very intense – so straight As or AAB at A level is a common entry grade requirement for the leading medical schools today. Certainly an A in chemistry is a great start, but most medical schools will look for high grades in at least one, more likely two, sciences at A level, plus another strong, academic subject. General studies is not considered a valid A level by medical schools. Increasingly, medical schools are also taking GCSE grades into account as another way to filter the growing number of straight-A students.

WHAT IF YOU DON'T HAVE ANY SCIENCE A LEVELS?

In theory, NHS Careers says you can still apply, but in practice, given the already stiff competition among students with science A levels, your chances are not great. The good news, however, is that a number of universities now offer pre-medical and pre-dental courses precisely for students with non-science A levels. These 'pre-' courses typically last 30 weeks and are designed to bring non-science students up to A-level standard in the three sciences.

HOW DO I FIND THE BEST COURSE FOR ME?

For courses on offer see Course Search at **www.ucas.com**.

Applicants are advised to use various resources of information in order to make their choices for higher education, including the Course Search facility and Stamford Test at **www.ucas.com**. League tables might be a component of this research but applicants should bear in mind that these tables attempt to rank institutions in an overall order, which reflects the interests, preoccupations and decisions of those who have produced and edited the tables. The ways in which they are compiled vary greatly and you will need to look closely at the criteria that have been used.

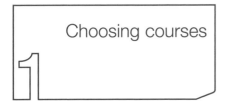

1 Choosing courses

Choosing courses

Use the UCAS website – www.ucas.com has lots of advice on how to find a course. Go to the students' section of the website for the best advice or go straight to Course Search to see all the courses available through UCAS. See the section on Entry Profiles on page 104 which explains what they are and how to use them. Our map of the UK at **www.ucas.com/students/choosingcourses/choosinguni/map/** shows you where all the universities and colleges are located.

Watch UCAStv – at **www.ucas.tv** there are videos on 'How to choose your course', 'Attending events' as well as case studies and video diaries from students talking about their experience of finding a course at university or college.

Attend UCAS conventions – UCAS conventions are held throughout the UK. Universities and colleges have exhibition stands where their staff offer information about their courses and institutions. Details of when the conventions are happening are shown at **www.ucas.com/events/conventions.**

Look at university and college websites and prospectuses – universities and colleges have prospectuses and course-specific leaflets on their undergraduate courses. Your school or college library may have copies or go to the university's website to download a copy or you can ask them to send one to you.

Go to university and college open days – most institutions offer open days to anyone who wants to attend. See the institution information pages on Course Search and the UCAS Open Days publication (see the Essential Reading chapter) for information on when they are taking place. Aim to visit all of the universities and colleges you are interested in before you apply. It will help with your expectations of university life and make sure the course is the right one for you.

League tables – these can be helpful but bear in mind that they attempt to rank institutions in an overall order reflecting the views of those that produce them. They may not reflect your views and needs. Examples can be found at **www.thecompleteuniversityguide.co.uk**, **www.guardian.co.uk/education/universityguide**, **www.thetimes.co.uk/gugs** (subscription service) and **www.thesundaytimes.co.uk/universityguide** (subscription service).

Visit the Unistats website at www.direct.gov.uk/unistats – it includes results from the National Student Survey and enables you to compare students' views of universities and colleges and the subjects they offer.

Do your research – speak and refer to as many trusted sources as you can find. Talk to someone already doing the job you have in mind. The section on "Which area?" on pages 12 will help you identify the different areas of medicine, dentistry and optometry you might want to enter.

UCAS CARD

If you're in Year 12, S5 or equivalent and thinking about higher education the UCAS Card's for you.
Sign up and you'll receive the following benefits...

- Save money on the high street with your UCAS discount card.
- Information about the courses and universities you're interested in.
- Free monthly newsletters providing advice on the application process.
- Expert help from our UCAS advisers with all the reminders, hints and tips.
- Chat with other students on **yougofurther.co.uk**, the UCAS student network.

Receive your free UCAS Card and all that goes with it by registering at **www.ucas.com/ucascard**.

DECIDING ON YOUR COURSE CHOICES

Through UCAS you can initially apply for up to five courses. How do you find out more information to make an informed decision?

Remember you don't have to make five course choices. Only apply for a course if you're completely happy with both the course and the university or college and you would definitely be prepared to accept a place.

How do you narrow down your course choices? First of all, look up course details in this book or on Course Search at **www.ucas.com**. This will give you an idea of the full range of courses and topics on offer. You'll quickly be able to eliminate institutions that don't offer the right course, or you can choose a 'hit list' of institutions first, and then see what they have to offer.

Once you've made a short(er) list, read the university and college Entry Profiles (see page 104) to find out what particular courses offer. You can then follow this up by looking at university or college websites, and generally finding out as much as you can about the course, department and institution. Don't be afraid to contact them to ask for more information, request their prospectus or arrange an open day visit.

Choosing courses

1

Entry Profiles

WHAT ARE THEY?

Entry Profiles give potential applicants to higher education specific information to help them make informed decisions about the courses they apply for. Detailed knowledge about the course, formal entry requirements and the qualities and experiences institutions are looking for in their applicants can help ensure that every applicant finds their way onto the right course. Entry Profiles are published on the UCAS website and can be reached using Course Search. They are available for all potential applicants and their advisers to see as they start making important decisions about where to apply. All course providers are asked to contribute Entry Profiles for the UCAS Course Search facility.

WHY USE THEM?

Courses can vary at different universities and colleges, even though they have the same name. Differences in course content, structure, optional modules, and the department's approach to teaching and learning can make the experience of studying any subject very different for students at different institutions, even before the size and location of the institution are taken into account.

It is important that you are fully informed about the courses and the institutions offering them before you apply, and that you know what academic qualifications and personal qualities are being sought in an applicant. Then you can avoid mistakes and make fully informed choices.

HOW DO I USE ENTRY PROFILES?

When you find courses that interest you, look for the EP symbol after the course title on Course Search at **www.ucas.com**. This means the course has an Entry Profile.

- First, read the information about the course. Does it cover subjects that interest you, and what career opportunities would be open to you? Does the Entry Profile tell you about the personal qualities the university or college is looking for in its students, or any experience that would be beneficial?
- Check the academic entry requirements. Are you studying the right subjects to be accepted onto this course? Will you meet the grades or Tariff points required? (See page 138 for information about the Tariff.)

- Make sure that you know where the course will be taught - sometimes it is not at the main campus. Could you travel to lectures and tutorials easily?
- Do you need to take an admissions test? If so, you need to find out how to apply for it, if there is a fee and where and when it will take place.
- Look for comments written by current or former students. What they have to say will help you get a feel for what it is like to be a student at that university or on that course.

If you don't find all the information you need in Course Search, check the universities' and colleges' websites or contact them direct with any questions you may have.

TOP TIP

Don't be afraid to pick up the phone – university and college admissions officers welcome enquiries directly from students, rather than careers officers phoning on your behalf. It shows you're genuinely interested and committed to your own career early on.

Choosing courses

1

Choosing your institution

Different people look for different things from their university or college course, but the checklist on the next page sets out the kinds of factors all prospective students should consider when choosing their university. Keep this list in mind on open days, when talking to friends about their experiences at various universities and colleges, or while reading prospectuses and websites.

WHAT TO CONSIDER WHEN CHOOSING YOUR MEDICINE OR DENTISTRY COURSE

Grades required	Use Course Search on the UCAS website, **www.ucas.com**, to view entry requirements for courses you are interested in. Also check out the university and college websites and prospectuses, or call up the medical/dental school admissions office. Some institutions specify grades required, eg AAB, while others specify points required, eg 340. If they ask for points it means they're using the UCAS Tariff system, which basically awards points to different types and levels of qualification. For example: An A grade at A level = 120 points; a B grade at A level = 100 points etc. The full Tariff is available at **www.ucas.com** and on pages 138–146.
Location	Do you want to stay close to home? Would you prefer to study at a city or campus university or college?
University 'ethos'	Find out if the medical/dental school is linked to a teaching hospital – which should mean that the hospital where you will spend your rotations will be more orientated towards (ie have more time for) medical students.
Prospects	You will generally get your first job in a hospital linked to the university, for example in one of the hospitals where you spent your rotation. Find out which hospitals have links with each medical school.
Cost	Ask the admissions office about variable tuition fees and financial assistance. (From your fifth year as a medical student, your fees will be paid by the Department of Health.)
Degree type	How is the course taught? Ask about the number of lectures per week, the amount of tutorials and one-to-one work, how you will be involved in project work.
Course assessment	What proportion of the assessment is based on your project work and how much is based on written assignments?
Facilities for medical/ dental students	For example, find out if there's a careers adviser dedicated to medical and dental students, or if there's a placements officer who takes charge of matching students to rotations.
'Fit'	Even if all the above criteria stack up, this one relies on gut feel – go and visit the institution if you can and see if it's 'you'.

Choosing courses

1

How will they choose you?

ADMISSIONS TESTS

Students applying to some courses are required to sit an admissions test as part of the application process. Details follow of some of the medicine and dentistry courses that use admissions tests as part of their selection criteria. This is not a definitive list, so check with the university or college for the most up-to-date information on their admissions tests. A list of tests can be found on **www.ucas.com/students/ choosingcourses/admissions**.

Admissions tests are a way to manage application numbers for high-demand courses by helping to differentiate fairly between well-qualified applicants. They can widen access and participation in higher education as they measure academic potential without being influenced by educational background.

Admissions tests broaden and complement other selection criteria as they often assess aptitude and reasoning rather than achievement and recall.

Admissions tests do not generally require additional teaching, although applicants should familiarise themselves with a specimen paper beforehand. Check with the test centre about what type of preparation is required. It is usually the applicant's own responsibility to ensure they are entered for a test by the closing date. Some tests are taken at the applicant's school or college, others require applicants to sit the test at a test centre or at the university or college as part of an interview day. Overseas applicants may not be required to sit an admissions test – check with the course provider.

Here are just some of the tests that are being used:

- Sixth Term Examination Papers (STEP)
- Special Tertiary Admissions Test (STAT) – used to assess a range of competencies commonly considered important for successful tertiary study
- Thinking Skills Assessment (TSA) – tests skills such as critical thinking and problem solving (not subject-specific)
- Institution's Own Test (IOT)
- BioMedical Admissions Test (BMAT)
- Graduate Medical Schools Admissions Test (GAMSAT)
- UK Clinical Aptitude Test (UKCAT)
- Medical School Admissions Test (MSAT).

Choosing courses

1

The 'BMAT'

BioMedical Admissions Test

WHICH UNIVERSITIES REQUIRE IT?

Currently four of the top UK universities require the BMAT. (Others also require it for entry to veterinary studies):

- University of Cambridge
- Imperial College London (University of London)
- University of Oxford
- University College London (University of London).

WHAT DOES IT INVOLVE?

A written test under exam conditions comprising three sections:

- 60 minutes multiple choice and short answer questionnaire to assess your aptitude and skills, ie how good you are at analysing and interpreting data
- 30 minutes multiple choice and short answer paper to test your scientific knowledge in biology, chemistry, physics and maths
- 30 minutes written task – essay on one of a choice of four topics.

WHERE IS THE TEST HELD?

The BMAT can be taken at your school or college, or one of several BMAT-approved test centres around the UK.

WHEN IS IT HELD?

Once a year, usually in October or November. In 2011,
the date is Wednesday 2 November at 09:00.

HOW CAN I REGISTER FOR THE TEST?

With the test centre direct. Ask you school or college
whether it is registered. If it is not, find a centre where
you can sit the test. To find a test centre go to
www.bmat.org.uk click on the 'Registration' tab and
then on 'Find a Centre'.

HOW MUCH DOES IT COST?

For candidates within the UK and EU, the Standard
BMAT fee for 2011 is £42.50. The closing date for
standard entries for 2011 is 30 September. Late entries
for the BMAT will be accepted until the 14 October
2011. A higher fee will apply.

HOW CAN I PREPARE?

By taking the sample tests on the website. The only bit
you can really cram for is the science paper but it
should be things you already know. The rest isn't testing
your knowledge so much as your analytical and logical
thinking ability.

WHERE CAN I GET MORE INFORMATION?

Go to the BioMedical Admissions Test website at
www.bmat.org.uk.

Choosing courses

1

The 'GAMSAT'

Graduate Medical School Admissions Test

The Graduate Medical School Admissions Test was pioneered in Australia by medical schools offering graduate entry programmes. Introduced into this country in 1999, it assists the selection for some graduate-entry programmes and is also used by Peninsula Medical School for certain applicants to its five-year course.

WHAT KIND OF TEST IS IT?

It is mostly multiple choice, emphasising reasoning ability and critical thinking. It actively encourages students to think outside obvious parameters when seeking solutions. The ability to apply conceptual thought under time-pressure and provide the best response is at the heart of the GAMSAT.

IS ANY SPECIFIC KNOWLEDGE NEEDED?

Scientific knowledge is necessary to understand the scenarios in question and terminology. The level of knowledge is quite high. In biology and chemistry it is roughly equivalent to first-year degree level, while in physics it's similar to A level.

WHAT QUALITIES ARE NEEDED TO SUCCEED?

Determination, flexibility of thought, scientific knowledge and the ability to write clearly and fluently are important. Analytical, logical thinking and an organised strategic approach when taking the test will also help.

WHAT WILL THE TEST BE LIKE?

The test has three parts:

1. Reasoning in humanities and social sciences

75 questions, 1 hour 40 minutes. Multiple-choice questions on passages to evaluate critical thinking and reasoning.

2. Written communication

Two 30-minute essays appraise the candidate's ability to draw concepts together and express them fluently in writing.

3. Reasoning in biological and physical sciences

110 questions, 2 hours 50 minutes. The focus of this part of the test is on passages and pictorial representations of data, measuring problem-solving skills, and the ability to offer hypotheses and reach reasoned conclusions.

Excellent scores in one section will not compensate for poor performance in another. Scores are valid for two years.

HOW MUCH DOES IT COST?

The standard fee to sit GAMSAT is £195.

WHICH UNIVERSITIES AND COLLEGES NEED IT?

- University of Nottingham at Derby
- St George's (University of London)
- Peninsula Dental School
- Peninsula Medical School
- University of Wales, Swansea
- Keele University.

WHERE CAN I GET MORE INFORMATION?

From UCAS on 01242 544 730, gamsat@ucas.ac.uk or the websites **www.ucas.com** and **www.gamsatuk.org**. Information booklets and practice tests are available from the UCAS online bookstore at **www.ucasbooks.com**.

WHEN AND WHERE DO I NEED TO TAKE THE TEST?

The test takes place on Friday 16 September 2011 at several locations in the UK. Registration is online at the website **www.gamsatuk.org** between 3 June and 12 August.

Choosing courses

1

The 'UKCAT'

UK Clinical Aptitude Test

The UK Clinical Aptitude Test (UKCAT) is used in the selection process by a consortium of medical and dental schools. The test helps universities make more informed choices among the many highly qualified applicants for their medical and dentistry programmes. Its aim is to ensure that the candidates selected have the most appropriate abilities, attitudes and professional behaviours.

WHAT KIND OF TEST IS IT?

It is designed to test aptitude rather than simply academic achievement. It tests the mental abilities and behavioural attributes that universities regard as important. It is taken on a computer, but requires minimal computer knowledge.

WHAT IS ITS STRUCTURE?

The test consists of four multiple-choice subtests:

- **verbal reasoning** – arriving at a reasoned conclusion from supplied written information
- **quantitative reasoning** – solving numerical problems
- **abstract reasoning** – assesses the ability to use both convergent and divergent thinking
- **decision analysis** – assesses the ability to deal with a variety of information, infer relationships, make judgements and respond appropriately in different situations.

HOW LONG DOES IT TAKE?

90 minutes.

HOW MUCH DOES IT COST?

The cost to sit the UKCAT is £65 for candidates in the EU before 31 August 2011 and £100 for other candidates. Between 1 September and 7 October 2011 the cost is £80 for candidates taking the UKCAT in the EU.

WHERE AND WHEN DO I TAKE IT?

There is no fixed date for sitting the exam but it must be taken before 8 October 2011 deadline for entry to participating universities in 2012 – or deferred entry in 2013. There are over 150 centres across the UK at which it can be taken. Registration is available online at **www.ukcat.ac.uk** together with details of fees and bursaries. Registration is from May to September and testing begins in July.

CAN I PREPARE MYSELF FOR THE TEST?

Coaching is not necessary, desirable or advantageous. The test is designed to be a test of aptitude rather than academic achievement, and therefore does not draw on any particular body of knowledge that a candidate can learn in advance. However candidates should familiarise themselves with the question styles and format of the test. A fully timed practice test is available from the UKCAT website.

WHICH DENTAL SCHOOLS NEED UKCAT?

- Queen's University Belfast
- Cardiff University
- University of Dundee
- University of Glasgow
- King's College London
- University of Manchester
- University of Newcastle
- Queen Mary, University of London
- University of Sheffield.

WHICH MEDICAL SCHOOLS NEED UKCAT?

- University of Aberdeen
- Barts and The London School of Medicine and Dentistry
- Brighton and Sussex Medical School
- Cardiff University
- University of Dundee
- University of Durham
- University of East Anglia
- University of Edinburgh
- University of Glasgow
- Hull York Medical School
- Imperial College London (graduate entry only)
- Keele University
- King's College London
- University of Leeds
- University of Leicester
- University of Manchester
- University of Newcastle
- University of Nottingham
- University of Oxford (graduate entry only)
- Peninsula College of Medicine and Dentistry
- Queen's University Belfast
- Queen Mary, University of London
- University of Sheffield
- University of Southampton
- University of St Andrews
- St George's, University of London
- University of Warwick (graduate entry only).

For full details visit **www.ukcat.ac.uk**.

Choosing courses

1

The cost of higher education

THE COST OF STUDYING IN THE UK

As a student, you will usually have to pay for two things: tuition fees for your course, which for most students do not need to be paid for up front, and living costs such as rent, food, books, transport and entertainment. Fees charged vary between courses, as well as between universities and colleges, so it's important to check these before you apply. The 2012 entry UCAS Course Search at **www.ucas.com/students/coursesearch** will be available from mid-May 2011. Course fee information will be added in mid-July for each course, or you can contact the universities and colleges direct.

If you're studying in Scotland and already live there, check the Student Awards Agency for Scotland (SAAS) website **www.saas.gov.uk** for further information.

STUDENT LOANS

The purpose of student loans from the Government is to help cover the costs of your tuition fees and basic living costs (rent, bills, food and so on). Two types are available: a tuition fee loan to cover the tuition charges and a maintenance loan to help with accommodation and other living costs. Both types of student loan are available to all students who meet the basic eligibility requirements. Interest will be charged at inflation (RPI) plus 3% while you are studying. In addition, many other commercial loans are available to students studying at university or college but the interest rate can vary considerably.

Find out more information from the relevant sites below:

England: Student Finance England -
www.direct.gov.uk/studentfinance
Northern Ireland: Student Finance Northern Ireland -
www.studentfinanceni.co.uk
Scotland: Student Awards Agency for Scotland -
www.saas.gov.uk
Wales: Student Finance Wales -
www.studentfinancewales.co.uk

IMPORTANT INFORMATION FOR STUDENTS
ENTERING ENGLISH UNIVERSITIES AND
COLLEGES FROM 1 SEPTEMBER 2012

At the time of writing, the Department for Business,
Innovation and Skills (BIS) has announced changes to
student finance, subject to parliamentary approval:

- Any university or college will be able to charge up to
  £6,000 a year for their courses. In exceptional cases,
  universities will be able to charge up to £9,000,
  subject to meeting much tougher conditions on
  widening participation and fair access.

- As is the case now, students in England will not have
  to pay up-front for their tuition, as Government loans
  will be available to most students. Students only start
  to repay these loans once they are earning over
  £21,000 per year.

- A new £150m National Scholarships Programme will
  be targeted at bright potential students from poor
  backgrounds.

- Students from families with incomes of up to
  £25,000 will be entitled to a non-repayable grant of
  £3,250 to help with living costs and those from
  families with incomes up to £42,600 will be entitled
  to a partial non-repayable grant.

- Loans to help with living costs will be available for
  all eligible students, irrespective of family income.

- Many universities and colleges will also offer non-
  repayable scholarships and bursaries to help
  students cover tuition and living costs whilst
  studying.

- All eligible part-time undergraduates who study for
  at least 25% of their time will be able to apply for a
  loan to cover the costs of their tuition, which means
  they no longer have to pay up front.

There will be extra support for disabled students and
students with child or adult dependants.

For more information on the proposed changes in
England, please visit
www.direct.gov.uk/studentfinance.

Connect with us...

 www.facebook.com/ucasonline

 www.twitter.com/ucas_online

 www.youtube.com/ucasonline

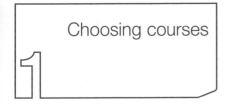

Choosing courses

1

International students

APPLYING TO STUDY IN THE UK

Deciding to go to university or college in the UK is very exciting. You need to think about what course to do, where to study, and how much it will cost. The decisions you make can have a huge effect on your future but UCAS is here to help.

HOW TO APPLY

Whatever your age or qualifications, if you want to apply for any of the 40,000 courses listed at over 300 universities and colleges on the UCAS website, you must apply through UCAS at **www.ucas.com**. If you are unsure, your school, college, adviser, or local British Council office will be able to help. Further advice and a video guide for international students can be found on the non-UK students' section of the UCAS website at **www.ucas.com/international**.

Students may apply on their own or through their school, college, adviser, or local British Council if this is registered with UCAS to use Apply. If you choose to use an education agent's services, check with the British Council to see if they hold a list of certificated or registered agents in your country. Check also on any charges you may need to pay. UCAS charges only the application fee (see below) but agents may charge for additional services.

HOW MUCH WILL MY APPLICATION COST?

If you choose to apply to more than one course, university or college you need to pay UCAS £22 GBP when you apply. If you only apply to one course at one university or college, you pay UCAS £11 GBP.

WHAT LEVEL OF ENGLISH?

UCAS provides a list of English language qualifications and grades that are acceptable to most UK universities and colleges, however you are advised to contact the institutions directly as each have their own entry requirement in English. For more information go to **www.ucas.com/students/wheretostart/nonukstudents/englangprof**.

INTERNATIONAL STUDENT FEES

If you study in the UK, your fee status (whether you pay full-cost fees or a subsidised fee rate) will be decided by the UK university or college you plan to attend. Before you decide which university or college to attend, you need to be absolutely certain that you can pay the full cost of:

- your tuition fees (the amount is set by universities and colleges, so contact them for more information – visit their websites where many list their fees. Fee details will also be included on Course Search at **www.ucas.com** from mid-July.)
- the everyday living expenses for you (and your family for the whole time that you are in the UK, including accommodation, food, heat, light, clothes, travel
- books and equipment for your course
- travel to and from your country.

You must include everything when you work out how much it will cost. You can get information to help you do this accurately from the international offices at universities and colleges, UKCISA (UK Council for International Student Affairs) and the British Council. There is a useful website tool to help you manage your money at university – **www.studentcalculator.org.uk**.

Scholarships and bursaries are offered at some universities and colleges and you should contact them for more information. In addition, you should check with your local British Council for additional scholarships available to students from your country who want to study in the UK.

LEGAL DOCUMENTS YOU WILL NEED

As you prepare to study in the UK, it is very important to think about the legal documents you will need to enter the country.

Everyone who comes to study in the UK needs a valid passport, details of which will be collected either in your UCAS application or later through Track. If you do not yet have a passport, you should apply for one as soon as possible. People from certain countries also need visas before they come into the UK. They are known as 'visa nationals'. You can check if you require a visa to travel to the UK by visiting the UK Border Agency website and selecting 'Studying in the UK', so please check the UK Border Agency website at **www.ukba.homeoffice.gov.uk** for the most up-to-date guidance and information about the United Kingdom's visa requirements.

When you apply for your visa you need to make sure you have the following documents:

- A confirmation of acceptance for studies (CAS) number from the university or college where you are going to study. The institution must be on the UKBA Register of Sponsors in order to accept international students
- A valid passport
- Evidence that you have enough money to pay for your course and living costs

- Certificates for all qualifications you have that are relevant to the course you have been accepted for and for any English language qualifications.

You will also have to give your biometric data.

Do check for further information from your local British Embassy or High Commission. Guidance information for international students is also available from UKCISA and from UKBA.

ADDITIONAL RESOURCES

There are a number of organisations that can provide further guidance and information to you as you prepare to study in the UK:

- British Council
  www.britishcouncil.org
- Education UK (British Council website dealing with educational matters)
  www.educationuk.org
- English UK (British Council accredited website listing English language courses in the UK)
  www.englishuk.com
- UK Border Agency (provides information on visa requirements and applications)
  www.ukba.homeoffice.gov.uk
- UKCISA (UK Council for International Student Affairs)
  www.ukcisa.org.uk
- BIS (Department for Business Innovation and Skills)
  www.bis.gov.uk
- Prepare for success
  www.prepareforsuccess.org.uk

Applying

2

Step 2 – Applying

You apply through UCAS using the online application system, called Apply, at **www.ucas.com**. You can apply for a maximum of five choices, but you don't have to use them all if you don't want to. If you apply for fewer than five choices, you can add more at a later date if you want to. But be aware of the course application deadlines.

IMPORTANT DATES FOR 2012 ENTRY	
Early June 2011	UCAS Apply opens for 2012 entry registration.
Mid-September 2011	Applications can be sent to UCAS.
15 October 2011	Application deadline for the receipt at UCAS of applications for all medicine, dentistry, veterinary medicine and veterinary science courses and for all courses at the universities of Oxford and Cambridge.
15 January 2012	Application deadline for the receipt at UCAS of applications for all courses except those listed above with a 15 October deadline, and some art and design courses with a 24 March deadline.
24 February 2012	Extra starts (see page 136 for more information about Extra).
24 March 2012	Application deadline for the receipt at UCAS of applications for art and design courses except those listed on Course Search at www.ucas.com with a 15 January deadline.
31 March 2012	If you apply by 15 January, the universities and colleges should aim to have sent their decisions by this date (but they can take longer).
10 May 2012	If you apply by 15 January, universities and colleges need to send their decisions by this date. If they don't, UCAS will make any outstanding choices unsuccessful on their behalf.
30 June 2012	Applications received after this date are entered into Clearing and are not automatically sent to universities and colleges (see page 150 for more information about Clearing).
4 July 2012	Last date to apply through Extra.
August 2012 (date to be confirmed)	Scottish Qualifications Authority (SQA) results are published.
16 August 2012	GCE and Advanced Diploma results are published (often known as 'A level results day'). Adjustment opens for registration (see page 151 for more information about Adjustment).

DON'T FORGET...

Universities and colleges guarantee to consider your application only if we receive it by the appropriate deadline. Check application deadlines for your courses on Course Search at www.ucas.com.

If you send it to UCAS after the deadline but before 30 June 2012, universities and colleges will consider your application only if they still have places available.

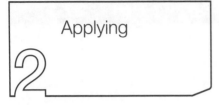

Applying

How to apply

You apply online at **www.ucas.com** through Apply – a secure, web-based application service that is designed for all our applicants, whether they are applying through a UCAS-registered centre or as an individual, anywhere in the world. Apply is:

- **easy to access** – all you need is an internet connection
- **easy to use** – you don't have to complete your application all in one go: you can save the sections as you complete them and come back to it later
- **easy to monitor** – once you've applied, you can use Track to check the progress of your application, including any decisions from universities or colleges. You can also reply to your offers using Track.

Watch the UCAStv guide to applying through UCAS at **www.ucas.tv**.

DEFERRED ENTRY

If you want to apply for deferred entry in 2013, perhaps because you want to take a year out between school or college and higher education, you should check that the university or college will accept a deferred entry application. Occasionally, tutors are not happy to accept students who take a gap year, because it interrupts the flow of their learning. If you apply for deferred entry, you must meet the conditions of any offers by 31 August 2012, unless otherwise agreed by the university or college. If you accept a place for 2013 entry and then change your mind, you cannot reapply through us in the 2013 entry cycle unless you withdraw your original application.

INVISIBILITY OF CHOICES

Universities and colleges cannot see details of the other choices on your application until you reply to any offers or you have not been successful at any of your choices. **You can submit only one UCAS application in each year's application cycle.**

APPLYING THROUGH YOUR SCHOOL OR COLLEGE

1 GET SCHOOL OR COLLEGE 'BUZZWORD'

Ask your UCAS application coordinator (may be your sixth form tutor) for your school or college UCAS 'buzzword'. This is a password for the school or college.

2 REGISTER

Go to **www.ucas.com/students/apply** and click on **Register/Log in to use Apply** and then **register**. After you have entered your registration details, the online system will automatically generate a username for you, but you'll have to come up with a password and answers to security questions.

3 COMPLETE SEVEN SECTIONS

Complete the sections of the application. To access any section, click on the section name at the top of the screen and follow the instructions. The sections are:

Personal details – contact details, residential status, disability status

Additional information – only UK applicants need to complete this section

Student finance – for UK students only

Choices – which courses you'd like to apply for

Education – your education to date

Employment – for example, work experience, holiday jobs

Personal statement – page 88.

Before you can send your application you need to go to the 'View all' screen and tick the 'section complete' box.

4 PASS TO REFEREE

Once you've completed all the sections, send your application electronically to your referee (normally your form tutor). They'll check it, approve it and add their reference to it, and will then send it to UCAS on your behalf.

USEFUL INFORMATION ABOUT APPLY

- Important details like date of birth and course codes will be checked by Apply. It will alert you if they are not valid.
- The text for your personal statement and reference can be copied and pasted into your application.
- From 2012 entry, if you want to, you will be able to enter European characters into certain areas of Apply.
- You can change your application at any time before it is completed and sent to UCAS.
- You can print and preview your application at any time. Before you send it you need to go to the 'View all' screen and tick the 'Section complete' box.
- Your school, college or centre can choose different payment methods. For example, they may want us to bill them, or you may be able to pay online by debit or credit card.

NOT APPLYING THROUGH A SCHOOL OR COLLEGE

If you're not currently studying, you'll probably be applying as an independent applicant rather than through a school, college or other UCAS-registered centre. In this case you won't be able to provide a 'buzzword', but we'll ask you a few extra questions to check you are eligible to apply.

If you're not applying through a UCAS-registered centre, the procedure you use for obtaining a reference will depend on whether or not you want your reference to be provided through a registered centre. For information on the procedures for providing references, visit **www.ucas.com/students/applying/howtoapply/reference**.

APPLICATION CHECKLIST

We want this to run smoothly for you and we also want
to process your application as quickly as possible. You
can help us to do this by remembering to do the
following:

✓ check the closing dates for applications – see
   page 122
✓ check the student finance information at
   www.ucas.com/students/studentfinance/
   and course fees information in Course Search at
   www.ucas.com (Course Search will be live from
   May 2011, whilst fees information will be available in
   mid-July 2011)
✓ start early and allow plenty of time for completing
   your application – including enough time for your
   referee to complete the reference section
✓ read the online instructions carefully before you start
✓ consider what each question is actually asking for –
   use the 'help'
✓ pay special attention to your personal statement (see
   page 128) and start drafting it early
✓ ask a teacher, parent, friend or careers adviser to
   review your draft application – particularly the
   personal statement
✓ if you get stuck, watch our videos on YouTube
   where we answer your frequently asked questions
   on completing a UCAS application at
   www.youtube.com/ucasonline
✓ if you have extra information that will not fit on your
   application, send it direct to your chosen universities
   or colleges after we have sent you your Welcome
   letter with your Personal ID – don't send it to us
✓ print a copy of the final version of your application, in
   case you are asked questions on it at an interview.

Applying

2

The personal statement

Next to choosing your courses, this section of your application will be the most time-consuming. It is of immense importance as many universities and colleges make their selection relying solely on the information in the UCAS application, rather than interviews and admissions tests. The personal statement can be the deciding factor in whether or not they offer you a place. If it is an institution that interviews, your statement could be the deciding factor in whether you get invited for interview.

Keep a copy of your personal statement – if you are called for interview, you will almost certainly be asked questions based on it.

Tutors will look carefully at your exam results, actual and predicted, your reference and your personal statement. Remember, they are looking for reasons to offer you a place – try to give them every opportunity to do so!

A SALES DOCUMENT

The personal statement is your opportunity to sell yourself, so do so. The university or college admissions tutor wants to get a rounded picture of you to decide whether you will make an interesting member of the university or college both academically and socially. They want to know more about you than the subjects you are studying at school.

HOW TO START

There are resources on **www.ucas.com** to help you, including a timeline, so that you start in good time, keep on track and give yourself a chance to get it all checked over and submitted on time. To help you with thinking about what should go in and how can it best represent your strengths, there is a mind map which will stretch your ideas and help you view things from all angles. Finally, you'll find a worksheet so that you're not starting off with just a blank sheet of paper, which can be very daunting indeed!

Include things like hobbies and work experience, and try to link the skills you have gained to the type of course you are applying for. Describe your career plans and goals. Have you belonged to sports teams or orchestras or held positions of responsibility in the community? Try to give evidence of your ability to undertake higher level study successfully by showing your commitment and maturity. If you left full-time education a while ago, talk about the work you have done and the skills you have gathered or how you have juggled bringing up a family with other activities – that is solid evidence of time management skills. Whoever you are, make sure you explain what appeals to you about the course you are applying for.

For courses in medicine it is important that you demonstrate excellent interpersonal skills and evidence that you have considered deeply your reasons for your choice of course. You should be able to describe some direct experience (or at least observation) of medical practice in the acute setting of a hospital or in a primary care/community setting, or better still, both.

Visit **www.ucas.tv** to view the video to help guide you through the process and address the most common fears and concerns about writing a personal statement.

WHAT ADMISSIONS TUTORS LOOK FOR	WHAT TO TELL THEM
<ul><li>Your reasons for wanting to take this subject in general and this particular course.</li><li>Your communication skills – not only what you say but how you say it. Your grammar and spelling must be perfect.</li><li>Relevant experience – practical things you've done that are related to your choice of course.</li><li>Evidence of your teamworking ability, leadership capability, independence.</li><li>Evidence of your skills, for example: IT skills, empathy and people skills, debating and public speaking, research and analysis.</li><li>Other activities that show your dedication and ability to apply yourself and maintain your motivation.</li></ul>	<ul><li>Why you want to do this subject – how you know it is the subject for you.</li><li>What experience you already have in this field – for example work experience, school projects, hobbies, voluntary work.</li><li>The skills and qualities you have as a person that would make you a good student, for example anything that shows your dedication, communication ability, academic achievement, initiative.</li><li>Examples that show you can knuckle down and apply yourself, for example running a marathon or your Extended Project.</li><li>If you're taking a gap year, why you've chosen this and (if possible) what you're going to do during it.</li><li>About your other interests and activities away from studying – to show you're a rounded person. (But remember that it is mainly your suitability for the particular course that they're looking to judge.)</li></ul>

WORK EXPERIENCE

How much does it count for? Ask any medical or dental admissions tutor about the importance of work experience on a candidate's application and they'll all agree – work experience shows a real, rather than theoretical, interest in your chosen profession. An absence of work experience might make tutors question your commitment to your choice of career.

Work experience is especially useful to help you find out what you want to do. Since medicine (even more than dentistry) is such a long course of study, it is important for you to find out early on whether it could really be a career for you. Given the choice, admissions tutors prefer to see examples of long-term work experience rather than the odd week here and there.

WHAT KINDS OF SCHEMES EXIST?

Once you're on your undergraduate course, your rotations, ie placements in various hospital departments, will automatically give you the experience you need. As a sixth former, the good news is that more and more universities and hospitals are running short work experience schemes, from **taster days** to formal periods of work observation or **shadowing schemes** in hospitals that allow you to 'shadow' a surgeon or doctor in a particular department. Competition for the in-hospital schemes is stiff, so you'll need to apply early. You'll also have to apply directly through the hospital's medical staffing or human resources departments. Taster schemes are usually offered on a first-come, first-served basis, and charge a fee. Ask your careers adviser to give you details of these schemes. Dental students should also try spending time at their local dental practice: for example, helping out in reception or as support for the dental nurses.

WHAT IF YOU'VE ONLY GOT NON-MEDICAL WORK EXPERIENCE?

Don't worry – it will still be useful to include it in your personal statement. The trick is to pull out the professional and personal skills you have developed that are of relevance to the work of a doctor or dentist.

WHICH WORK EXPERIENCE?

Examples of the kinds of work experience of use to your medical/dental school application:

- shadowing a hospital doctor
- helping out in a care home
- working on reception or as support to dental nurses in a local dental practice
- working as a first-aider in Scouts
- working as a hospital auxiliary.

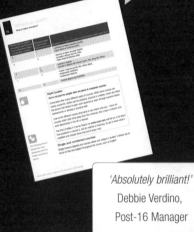

Offers

3

Step 3 – Offers

Once we have sent your application to your chosen universities and colleges, they will all consider it independently and tell us if they can offer you a place. Some universities and colleges will take longer to make decisions than others. You may be asked to attend an interview, sit an additional test or provide a piece of work, such as an essay, before a decision can be made.

Many universities (particularly the more popular ones, running competitive courses) use interviews as part of their selection process. Universities will want to find out why you want to study your chosen course at their institution, and they can make sure the course is suitable for you and your future career plans. Interviews also give you an opportunity to ask the university any questions you may have about the course or their institution.

If you are called for interview, the key areas they are likely to cover will be:

- evidence of your academic/scientific ability
- your capacity to study hard
- your commitment to a career in medicine, dentistry or optometry, best shown by work experience
- your awareness of current issues that may have an impact on your chosen field of study
- your manual dexterity, if applying for dentistry, optometry or surgery
- your interpersonal skills.

A lot of the interview will be based on information on your application, especially your personal statement. See pages 128 for tips about the personal statement.

SAMPLE INTERVIEW QUESTIONS

- How would you feel about treating a heavy smoker suffering from cancer?
  (To explore your approach to 'ethical' issues.)
- Can you give us some examples of your manual dexterity?
  (Good answers include playing the piano, model making or sewing.)
- What do you think of the changes to junior doctors' working hours?
  (To test your awareness of what's going on in your chosen field.)

Whenever a university or college makes a decision about your application, we record it and let you know. You can check the progress of your application using Track at **www.ucas.com**. This is our secure online service which gives you access to your application, using the same username and password you used when you applied. You can use it to find out if you have been invited for an interview or need to provide an additional piece of work, and you can check to see if you have received any offers.

TYPES OF OFFER

Universities can make two types of offer: conditional or unconditional.

Conditional offer

A conditional offer means the university or college is willing to offer you a place if you meet certain conditions – usually based on exam results. The conditions may be based on Tariff points (for example, 300 points from three A levels), or specify certain grades in named subjects (for example, A in chemistry, B in biology, C in mathematics).

Unconditional offer

If you've met all the academic requirements for the course and the university or college wants to accept you, they will make you an unconditional offer. If you accept this you'll have a definite place.

However, for both types of offer, there might be other requirements, like medical or financial conditions, that you need to meet before you can start your course.

REPLYING TO OFFERS

When you have received decisions for all your choices, you must decide what you want to accept. You will be given a deadline in Track by which you have to make your replies. Before replying, get advice from family, friends or advisers, but remember that you're the one taking the course so it's your decision.

Firm acceptance

- Your firm acceptance is your first choice - this is your preferred choice out of all the offers you have received. You can only have one firm acceptance.
- If you accept an unconditional offer, you are agreeing that you will attend the course, so you must decline any other offers.
- If you accept a conditional offer, you are agreeing that you will attend the course at that university or college if you meet the conditions of the offer. You can accept another offer as an insurance choice.

Insurance acceptance

- If your firm acceptance is a conditional offer, you can accept another offer as an insurance choice. Your insurance choice can be conditional or unconditional and acts as a back-up, so if you don't meet the conditions for your firm choice but meet the conditions for your insurance, you will be committed to the insurance choice. You can only have one insurance choice.
- The conditions for your insurance choice would usually be lower than your firm choice.
- You don't have to accept an insurance choice if you don't want one.

For more information watch our video guides How to use Track, Making sense of your offers, and How to reply to your offers at **www.ucas.tv**.

WHAT IF YOU HAVE NO OFFERS?

If you have used all five choices on your application and either received no offers, or decided to turn down any offers you have received, you may be eligible to apply for another choice through Extra. Find out more about Extra on page 136.

If you are not eligible for Extra, in the summer you can contact universities and colleges with vacancies in Clearing. See page 150 for more information.

3 | Offers

Extra

Extra allows you to make additional choices, one at a time, without having to wait for Clearing in July. It is completely optional and free, and is designed to encourage you to continue researching and choosing courses if you are holding no offers. The courses available through Extra will be highlighted on Course Search, at www.ucas.com. The Extra service is available to eligible applicants from 24 February to early July 2012 through Track at **www.ucas.com**.

WHO IS ELIGIBLE?

You will be eligible for Extra if you have already made five choices and:

- you have had unsuccessful or withdrawal decisions from all five of your choices, or
- you have cancelled your outstanding choices and hold no offers, or
- you have received decisions from all five choices and have declined all offers made to you.

HOW DOES IT WORK?

We contact you and explain what to do if you are eligible for Extra. If you are eligible a special Extra button will be available on your Track screen. If you want to use Extra you should:

- check on Course Search for courses that are available through Extra; they are shown by the symbol X after the course title
- choose one that you would like to apply for and enter the details on your Track screen.

When you have chosen a course the university or college will be able to view your application and consider you for its course.

WHAT HAPPENS NEXT?

We give the universities and colleges a maximum of 21 days to consider your Extra application. During this time, you cannot be considered by another university or college. If you have not heard after 21 days you can refer yourself to a different university or college if you wish, but it is a good idea to ring the one currently considering you before doing so. If you are made an offer, you can choose whether or not to accept it.

If you accept any offer, conditional or unconditional, you will not be able to take any further part in Extra.

If you are currently studying for examinations, any offer that you receive is likely to be an offer conditional on exam grades. If you already have your examination results, it is possible that a university or college may make an unconditional offer. If you accept an unconditional offer, you will be placed. If you decide to decline the offer or the university or college decides they cannot make you an offer, you will be given another opportunity to use Extra, time permitting. Your Extra button on Track will be reactivated.

Once you have accepted an offer in Extra, you are committed to it in the same way as you would be with an offer through the main UCAS system. Conditional offers made through Extra will be treated in the same way as other conditional offers, when your examination results become available.

If your results do not meet the conditions and the university or college decides that they cannot confirm your Extra offer, you will automatically become eligible for Clearing if it is too late for you to be considered by another university or college in Extra.

If you are unsuccessful, decline an offer, or do not receive an offer, or 21 days have elapsed since choosing a course through Extra, you can use Extra to apply for another course, time permitting.

ADVICE

Do the same careful research and seek guidance on your Extra choice of university or college and course as you did for your initial choices. If you applied to high-demand courses and institutions in your original application and were unsuccessful, you could consider related or alternative subjects or perhaps apply for the subject you want in combination with another. Your teachers or careers advisers or the universities and colleges themselves can provide useful guidance. Entry Profiles, which appear with most courses listed on Course Search, are another important source of information. Be flexible, that is the key to success. But you are the only one who know how flexible you are prepared to be. Remember that even if you decide to take a degree course other than medicine or dentistry, you may be able to take the postgraduate route into the profession.

Visit **www.ucas.tv** to watch the video guide on how to use Extra.

Offers

3

The Tariff

Admission to higher education courses is generally dependent upon an individual's achievement in level 3 qualifications, such as GCE A levels. Did you know that there are currently over 3,000 level 3 qualifications available in the UK alone?

As if the number of qualifications available was not confusing enough, different qualifications can have different grading structures (alphabetical, numerical or a mixture of both). Finding out what qualifications are needed for different higher education courses can be very confusing.

The UCAS Tariff is the system for allocating points to qualifications used for entry to higher education. It allows students to use a range of different qualifications to help secure a place on an undergraduate course.

Universities and colleges use the UCAS Tariff to make comparisons between applicants with different

qualifications. Tariff points are often used in entry requirements, although other factors are often taken into account. Entry Profiles provide a fuller picture of what admissions tutors are seeking.

The tables on the following pages show the qualifications covered by the UCAS Tariff. There may have been changes to these tables since this book was printed. You should visit **www.ucas.com** to view the most up-to-date tables.

FURTHER INFORMATION?

Although Tariff points can be accumulated in a variety of ways, not all of these will necessarily be acceptable for entry to a particular higher education course. The achievement of a points score therefore does not give an automatic entitlement to entry, and many other factors are taken into account in the admissions process.

The Course Search facility at **www.ucas.com** is the best source of reference to find out what qualifications are acceptable for entry to specific courses. Updates to the Tariff, including details on how new qualifications are added, can be found at **www.ucas.com/students/ucas_tariff/.**

HOW DOES THE TARIFF WORK?

- Students can collect Tariff points from a range of different qualifications, eg GCE A level with BTEC Nationals.
- There is no ceiling to the number of points that can be accumulated.
- There is no double counting. Certain qualifications within the Tariff build on qualifications in the same subject. In these cases only the qualification with the higher Tariff score will be counted. This principle applies to:
  - GCE Advanced Subsidiary level and GCE Advanced level
  - Scottish Highers and Advanced Highers
  - Speech, drama and music awards at grades 6, 7 and 8.
- Tariff points for the Advanced Diploma come from the Progression Diploma score plus the relevant Additional and Specialist Learning (ASL) Tariff points. Please see the appropriate qualification in the Tariff tables to calculate the ASL score.
- The Extended Project Tariff points are included within the Tariff points for Progression and Advanced Diplomas. Extended Project points represented in the Tariff only count when the qualification is taken outside of these Diplomas.
- Where the Tariff tables refer to specific awarding organisations, only qualifications from these awarding organisations attract Tariff points. Qualifications with a similar title, but from a different qualification awarding organisation do not attract Tariff points.

HOW DO UNIVERSITIES AND COLLEGES USE THE TARIFF?

The Tariff provides a facility to help universities and colleges when expressing entrance requirements and when making conditional offers. Entry requirements and conditional offers expressed as Tariff points will often require a minimum level of achievement in a specified subject (for example '300 points to include grade A at A level chemistry', or '260 points including SQA Higher grade B in mathematics').

Use of the Tariff may also vary from department to department at any one institution, and may in some cases be dependent on the programme being offered.

In July 2010, UCAS announced plans to review the Tariff. This review will take between 18 months and two years. You can read more about the review at www.ucas.com/qireview.

WHAT QUALIFICATIONS ARE INCLUDED IN THE TARIFF?

The following qualifications are included in the UCAS Tariff. See the number on the qualification title to find the relevant section of the Tariff table.

1   AAT NVQ level 3 in Accounting
2   AAT level 3 Diploma in Accounting (QCF)
3   Advanced Diploma
4   Advanced Extension Awards
5   Advanced Placement Programme (US and Canada)
6   Arts Award (Gold)
7   ASDAN Community Volunteering qualification
8   Asset Languages Advanced Stage
9   British Horse Society (Stage 3 Horse Knowledge & Care, Stage 3 Riding and Preliminary Teacher's Certificate)
10   BTEC Awards (NQF)
11   BTEC Certificates and Extended Certificates (NQF)
12   BTEC Diplomas (NQF)
13   BTEC National in Early Years (NQF)
14   BTEC Nationals (NQF)
15   BTEC QCF Qualifications
16   CACHE Award, Certificate and Diploma in Child Care and Education
17   Cambridge ESOL Examinations
18   Cambridge Pre-U
19   CISI Introduction to Securities and Investment
20   Certificate of Personal Effectiveness (COPE)
21   Diploma in Fashion Retail
22   Diploma in Foundation Studies (Art & Design; Art, Design & Media)
23   EDI Level 3 Certificate in Accounting, Certificate in Accounting (IAS)
24   Essential Skills (Northern Ireland)
25   Essential Skills Wales
26   Extended Project (stand alone)
27   Free-standing Mathematics
28   Functional skills
29   GCE (AS, AS Double Award, A level, A level Double Award and A level (with additional AS))
30   Hong Kong Diploma of Secondary Education (from 2012 entry onwards)
31   ifs School of Finance (Certificate and Diploma in Financial Studies)
32   iMedia (OCR level Certificate/Diploma for iMedia Professionals)
33   International Baccalaureate (IB) Diploma
34   International Baccalaureate (IB) Certificate
35   Irish Leaving Certificate (Higher and Ordinary levels)
36   IT Professionals (iPRO) (Certificate and Diploma)
37   Key Skills (Levels 2, 3 and 4)
38   Music examinations (grades 6, 7 and 8)
39   NPTC Level 3 Land Based Qualifications
40   OCR Level 3 Certificate in Mathematics for Engineering
41   OCR Level 3 Certificate for Young Enterprise
42   OCR Nationals (National Certificate, National Diploma and National Extended Diploma)
43   Principal Learning Wales
44   Progression Diploma
45   Scottish Qualifications
46   Speech and Drama examinations (grades 6, 7 and 8 and Performance Studies)
47   Sports Leaders UK
48   Welsh Baccalaureate Advanced Diploma (Core)

UCAS TARIFF TABLES

1

AAT NVQ LEVEL 3 IN ACCOUNTING	
GRADE	TARIFF POINTS
PASS	160

2

AAT LEVEL 3 DIPLOMA IN ACCOUNTING	
GRADE	TARIFF POINTS
PASS	160

3

ADVANCED DIPLOMA

Advanced Diploma = Progression Diploma plus Additional & Specialist Learning (ASL). Please see the appropriate qualification to calculate the ASL score. Please see the Progression Diploma (Table 44) for Tariff scores

4

ADVANCED EXTENSION AWARDS	
GRADE	TARIFF POINTS
DISTINCTION	40
MERIT	20

Points for Advanced Extension Awards are over and above those gained from the A level grade

5

ADVANCED PLACEMENT PROGRAMME (US & CANADA)	
GRADE	TARIFF POINTS
Group A	
5	120
4	90
3	60
Group B	
5	50
4	35
3	20

Details of the subjects covered by each group can be found at www.ucas.com/students/ucas_tariff/tarifftables

6

ARTS AWARD (GOLD)	
GRADE	TARIFF POINTS
PASS	35

7

ASDAN COMMUNITY VOLUNTEERING QUALIFICATION	
GRADE	TARIFF POINTS
CERTIFICATE	50
AWARD	30

8

ASSET LANGUAGES ADVANCED STAGE			
GRADE	TARIFF POINTS	GRADE	TARIFF POINTS
Speaking		Listening	
GRADE 12	28	GRADE 12	25
GRADE 11	20	GRADE 11	18
GRADE 10	12	GRADE 10	11
Reading		Writing	
GRADE 12	25	GRADE 12	25
GRADE 11	18	GRADE 11	18
GRADE 10	11	GRADE 10	11

9

BRITISH HORSE SOCIETY	
GRADE	TARIFF POINTS
Stage 3 Horse Knowledge & Care	
PASS	35
Stage 3 Riding	
PASS	35
Preliminary Teacher's Certificate	
PASS	35

Awarded by Equestrian Qualifications (GB) Ltd (EQL)

10

BTEC AWARDS (NQF) (EXCLUDING BTEC NATIONAL QUALIFICATIONS)			
GRADE	TARIFF POINTS		
	Group A	Group B	Group C
DISTINCTION	20	30	40
MERIT	13	20	26
PASS	7	10	13

Details of the subjects covered by each group can be found at www.ucas.com/students/ucas_tariff/tarifftables

11

BTEC CERTIFICATES AND EXTENDED CERTIFICATES (NQF) (EXCLUDING BTEC NATIONAL QUALIFICATIONS)					
GRADE	TARIFF POINTS				
	Group A	Group B	Group C	Group D	Extended Certificates
DISTINCTION	40	60	80	100	60
MERIT	26	40	52	65	40
PASS	13	20	26	35	20

Details of the subjects covered by each group can be found at www.ucas.com/students/ucas_tariff/tarifftables

12

BTEC DIPLOMAS (NQF) (EXCLUDING BTEC NATIONAL QUALIFICATIONS)			
GRADE	TARIFF POINTS		
	Group A	Group B	Group C
DISTINCTION	80	100	120
MERIT	52	65	80
PASS	26	35	40

Details of the subjects covered by each group can be found at www.ucas.com/students/ucas_tariff/tarifftables

13

BTEC NATIONAL IN EARLY YEARS (NQF)						
GRADE	TARIFF POINTS	GRADE	TARIFF POINTS	GRADE	TARIFF POINTS	
Theory				Practical		
Diploma		Certificate		D	120	
DDD	320	DD	200	M	80	
DDM	280	DM	160	P	40	
DMM	240	MM	120			
MMM	220	MP	80			
MMP	160	PP	40			
MPP	120					
PPP	80					

Points apply to the following qualifications only: BTEC National Diploma in Early Years (100/1279/5); BTEC National Certificate in Early Years (100/1280/1).

14

BTEC NATIONALS (NQF)						
GRADE	TARIFF POINTS	GRADE	TARIFF POINTS	GRADE	TARIFF POINTS	
Diploma		Certificate		Award		
DDD	360	DD	240	D	120	
DDM	320	DM	200	M	80	
DMM	280	MM	160	P	40	
MMM	240	MP	120			
MMP	200	PP	80			
MPP	160					
PPP	120					

15

BTEC QUALIFICATIONS (QCF) (SUITE OF QUALIFICATIONS KNOWN AS NATIONALS)				
EXTENDED DIPLOMA	DIPLOMA	SUBSIDIARY DIPLOMA	CERTIFICATE	TARIFF POINTS
D*D*D*				420
D*D*D				400
D*DD				380
DDD				360
DDM				320
DMM	D*D*			280
	D*D			260
MMM	DD			240
MMP	DM			200
MPP	MM			160
		D*		140
PPP	MP	D		120
	PP	M		80
			D*	70
			D	60
		P	M	40
			P	20

UCAS TARIFF TABLES

16

CACHE LEVEL 3 AWARD, CERTIFICATE AND DIPLOMA IN CHILD CARE & EDUCATION

AWARD		CERTIFICATE		DIPLOMA	
GRADE	TARIFF POINTS	GRADE	TARIFF POINTS	GRADE	TARIFF POINTS
A	30	A	110	A	360
B	25	B	90	B	300
C	20	C	70	C	240
D	15	D	55	D	180
E	10	E	35	E	120

17

CAMBRIDGE ESOL EXAMINATIONS

GRADE	TARIFF POINTS
Certificate of Proficiency in English	
A	140
B	110
C	70
Certificate in Advanced English	
A	70

18

CAMBRIDGE PRE-U

GRADE	TARIFF POINTS	GRADE	TARIFF POINTS	GRADE	TARIFF POINTS
Principal Subject		Global Perspectives and Research		Short Course	
D1	TBC	D1	TBC	D1	TBC
D2	145	D2	140	D2	TBC
D3	130	D3	126	D3	60
M1	115	M1	112	M1	53
M2	101	M2	98	M2	46
M3	87	M3	84	M3	39
P1	73	P1	70	P1	32
P2	59	P2	56	P2	26
P3	46	P3	42	P3	20

19

CISI INTRODUCTION TO SECURITIES AND INVESTMENT

GRADE	TARIFF POINTS
PASS WITH DISTINCTION	60
PASS WITH MERIT	40
PASS	20

20

CERTIFICATE OF PERSONAL EFFECTIVENESS (COPE)

GRADE	TARIFF POINTS
PASS	70

Points are awarded for the Certificate of Personal Effectiveness (CoPE) awarded by ASDAN and CCEA

21

DIPLOMA IN FASHION RETAIL

GRADE	TARIFF POINTS
DISTINCTION	160
MERIT	120
PASS	80

Awarded by ABC Awards

22

DIPLOMA IN FOUNDATION STUDIES (ART & DESIGN AND ART, DESIGN & MEDIA)

GRADE	TARIFF POINTS
DISTINCTION	285
MERIT	225
PASS	165

Awarded by ABC, Edexcel, UAL and WJEC

23

EDI LEVEL 3 CERTIFICATE IN ACCOUNTING, CERTIFICATE IN ACCOUNTING (IAS)

GRADE	TARIFF POINTS
DISTINCTION	120
MERIT	90
PASS	70

24

ESSENTIAL SKILLS (NORTHERN IRELAND)

GRADE	TARIFF POINTS
LEVEL 2	10

Details of the subjects covered by each group can be found at www.ucas.com/students/ ucas_tariff/tarifftables

25

ESSENTIAL SKILLS WALES

GRADE	TARIFF POINTS
LEVEL 3	20
LEVEL 2	10

Only allocated at level 2 if studied as part of a wider composite qualification such as 14-19 Diploma or Welsh Baccalaureate

26

EXTENDED PROJECT (STAND ALONE)

GRADE	TARIFF POINTS
A*	70
A	60
B	50
C	40
D	30
E	20

Points for the Extended Project cannot be counted if taken as part of Progression/Advanced Diploma

27

FREE-STANDING MATHEMATICS

GRADE	TARIFF POINTS
A	20
B	17
C	13
D	10
E	7

Covers free-standing Mathematics - Additional Maths, Using and Applying Statistics, Working with Algebraic and Graphical Techniques, Modelling with Calculus

UCAS TARIFF TABLES

28

FUNCTIONAL SKILLS

GRADE	TARIFF POINTS
LEVEL 2	10

Only allocated if studied as part of a wider composite qualification such as 14-19 Diploma or Welsh Baccalaureate

29

GCE AND VCE

GRADE	TARIFF POINTS	GRADE	TARIFF POINTS	GRADE	TARIFF POINTS	GRADE	TARIFF POINTS	GRADE	TARIFF POINTS
GCE & AVCE Double Award		GCE A level with additional AS (9 units)		GCE A level & AVCE		GCE AS Double Award		GCE AS & AS VCE	
A*A*	280	A*A	200	A*	140	AA	120	A	60
A*A	260	AA	180	A	120	AB	110	B	50
AA	240	AB	170	B	100	BB	100	C	40
AB	220	BB	150	C	80	BC	90	D	30
BB	200	BC	140	D	60	CC	80	E	20
BC	180	CC	120	E	40	CD	70		
CC	160	CD	110			DD	60		
CD	140	DD	90			DE	50		
DD	120	DE	80			EE	40		
DE	100	EE	60						
EE	80								

30

HONG KONG DIPLOMA OF SECONDARY EDUCATION

GRADE	TARIFF POINTS	GRADE	TARIFF POINTS	GRADE	TARIFF POINTS
All subjects except mathematics		Mathematics compulsory component		Mathematics optional components	
5**	No value	5**	No value	5**	No value
5*	130	5*	60	5*	70
5	120	5	45	5	60
4	80	4	35	4	50
3	40	3	25	3	40

Points come into effect for entry to higher education from 2012 onwards. No value for 5** pending receipt of candidate evidence (post 2012)

31

IFS SCHOOL OF FINANCE (NQF & QCF)

GRADE	TARIFF POINTS	GRADE	TARIFF POINTS
Certificate in Financial Studies (CeFS)		Diploma in Financial Studies (DipFS)	
A	60	A	60
B	50	B	50
C	40	C	40
D	30	D	30
E	20	E	20

Completion of both qualifications will result in a maximum of 120 UCAS Tariff points

32

LEVEL 3 CERTIFICATE / DIPLOMA FOR iMEDIA USERS (iMEDIA)

GRADE	TARIFF POINTS
DIPLOMA	66
CERTIFICATE	40

Awarded by OCR

UCAS TARIFF TABLES

33

INTERNATIONAL BACCALAUREATE (IB) DIPLOMA

GRADE	TARIFF POINTS	GRADE	TARIFF POINTS
45	720	34	479
44	698	33	457
43	676	32	435
42	654	31	413
41	632	30	392
40	611	29	370
39	589	28	348
38	567	27	326
37	545	26	304
36	523	25	282
35	501	24	260

34

INTERNATIONAL BACCALAUREATE (IB) CERTIFICATE

GRADE	TARIFF POINTS	GRADE	TARIFF POINTS	GRADE	TARIFF POINTS
Higher Level		Standard Level		Core	
7	130	7	70	3	120
6	110	6	59	2	80
5	80	5	43	1	40
4	50	4	27	0	10
3	20	3	11		

35

IRISH LEAVING CERTIFICATE

GRADE	TARIFF POINTS	GRADE	TARIFF POINTS
Higher		Ordinary	
A1	90	A1	39
A2	77	A2	26
B1	71	B1	20
B2	64	B2	14
B3	58	B3	7
C1	52		
C2	45		
C3	39		
D1	33		
D2	26		
D3	20		

36

IT PROFESSIONALS (iPRO)

GRADE	TARIFF POINTS
DIPLOMA	100
CERTIFICATE	80

Awarded by OCR

37

KEY SKILLS

GRADE	TARIFF POINTS
LEVEL 4	30
LEVEL 3	20
LEVEL 2	10

Details of the subjects covered by each group can be found at www.ucas.com/students/ucas_tariff/tarifftables

38

MUSIC EXAMINATIONS

GRADE	TARIFF POINTS	GRADE	TARIFF POINTS	GRADE	TARIFF POINTS
Practical					
Grade 8		Grade 7		Grade 6	
DISTINCTION	75	DISTINCTION	60	DISTINCTION	45
MERIT	70	MERIT	55	MERIT	40
PASS	55	PASS	40	PASS	25
Theory					
Grade 8		Grade 7		Grade 6	
DISTINCTION	30	DISTINCTION	20	DISTINCTION	15
MERIT	25	MERIT	15	MERIT	10
PASS	20	PASS	10	PASS	5

Points shown are for the ABRSM, Guildhall, LCMM, Rockschool and Trinity College London Advanced level

UCAS TARIFF TABLES

39

NPTC LEVEL 3 LAND BASED QUALIFICATIONS				
EXTENDED DIPLOMA	DIPLOMA	SUBSIDIARY DIPLOMA	CERTIFICATE	TARIFF POINTS
D				360
M	D			240
	M			160
P		D		120
	P	M		80
			D	60
		P	M	40
			P	20

Points come into effect for entry to higher education from 2011 onwards.

40

OCR LEVEL 3 CERTIFICATE IN MATHEMATICS FOR ENGINEERING	
GRADE	TARIFF POINTS
A*	TBC
A	90
B	75
C	60
D	45
E	30

41

OCR LEVEL 3 CERTIFICATE FOR YOUNG ENTERPRISE	
GRADE	TARIFF POINTS
DISTINCTION	40
MERIT	30
PASS	20

42

OCR NATIONALS					
GRADE	TARIFF POINTS	GRADE	TARIFF POINTS	GRADE	TARIFF POINTS
National Extended Diploma		National Diploma		National Certificate	
D1	360	D	240	D	120
D2/M1	320	M1	200	M	80
M2	280	M2/P1	160	P	40
M3	240	P2	120		
P1	200	P3	80		
P2	160				
P3	120				

43

PRINCIPAL LEARNING WALES	
GRADE	TARIFF POINTS
A*	210
A	180
B	150
C	120
D	90
E	60

Points for Principal Learning Wales come into effect for entry to higher education from 2011 onwards.

44

PROGRESSION DIPLOMA	
GRADE	TARIFF POINTS
A*	350
A	300
B	250
C	200
D	150
E	100

Advanced Diploma = Progression Diploma plus Additional & Specialist Learning (ASL). Please see the appropriate qualification to calculate the ASL score.

45

SCOTTISH QUALIFICATIONS							
GRADE	TARIFF POINTS	GRADE	TARIFF POINTS	GRADE	TARIFF POINTS	GROUP	TARIFF POINTS
Advanced Higher		Higher		Scottish Interdisciplinary Project		Scottish National Certificates	
A	130	A	80	A	65	C	125
B	110	B	65	B	55	B	100
C	90	C	50	C	45	A	75
D	72	D	36				
Ungraded Higher		NPA PC Passport					
PASS	45	PASS	45				
		Core Skills					
		HIGHER	20				

Details of the subjects covered by each Scottish National Certificate can be found at www.ucas.com/students/ucas_tariff/tarifftables

UCAS TARIFF TABLES

46

SPEECH AND DRAMA EXAMINATIONS							
GRADE	TARIFF POINTS	GRADE	TARIFF POINTS	GRADE	TARIFF POINTS	GRADE	TARIFF POINTS
PCertLAM		Grade 8		Grade 7		Grade 6	
DISTINCTION	90	DISTINCTION	65	DISTINCTION	55	DISTINCTION	40
MERIT	80	MERIT	60	MERIT	50	MERIT	35
PASS	60	PASS	45	PASS	35	PASS	20

Points shown are for ESB, LAMDA, LCMM and Trinity Guildhall Advanced level speech and drama examinations accredited in the National Qualifications Framework and LAMDA'S Certificates in Communication and Certificate in Performance accredited on the Qualifications and Credit framework (QCF). Tariff points are available for both the NQF and QCF PCertLAM.

47

SPORTS LEADERS UK	
GRADE	TARIFF POINTS
PASS	30

These points are awarded to Higher Sports Leader Award and Level 3 Certificate in Higher Sports Leadership (QCF)

48

WELSH BACCALAUREATE ADVANCED DIPLOMA (CORE)	
GRADE	TARIFF POINTS
PASS	120

These points are awarded only when a candidate achieves the Welsh Baccalaureate Advanced Diploma

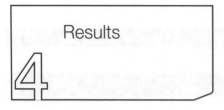

Results

4

Step 4 – Results

We receive many exam results direct from the exam boards – check the list at **www.ucas.com**. If your qualification is listed, you don't need to send your results to us or the universities and colleges where you're holding offers. Check Track at **www.ucas.com** to see if you've got a place on your chosen course.

If your qualification is listed, we send your results to the universities and colleges that you have accepted as your firm and insurance choices. If your qualification is not listed, you must send your exam results to the universities and colleges where you are holding offers.

You should arrange your holidays so that you are at home when your exam results are published because, if there are any issues to discuss, admissions tutors will want to speak to you in person.

After you have received your exam results check Track to find out if you have a place on your chosen course.

If you have met all the conditions for your firm choice, the university or college will confirm that you have a place. Sometimes, they may still confirm you have a place even if you have not quite met all the offer conditions; or they may offer you a place on a similar course.

If you have not met the conditions of your firm choice and the university or college has not confirmed your place, but you have met all the conditions of your insurance offer, the university or college will confirm that you have a place.

When a university or college tells us that you have a place, we send you confirmation by letter.

RE-MARKED EXAMS

If you ask for any of your exams to be re-marked, you must tell the universities and colleges where you're holding offers. If a university or college cannot confirm your place based on the initial results, you should ask them if they would be able to reconsider their decision after the re-mark. They don't have to reconsider their position even if your re-mark results in higher grades. Don't forget that re-marks may also result in lower grades.

The exam boards tell us about any re-marks that result in grade changes. We then send the revised grades to the universities and colleges where you're holding offers. As soon as you know about grade changes, you should also tell these universities and colleges.

'CASHING IN' A LEVEL RESULTS

If you have taken A levels, your school or college must certificate or 'cash in' all your unit scores before the exam board can award final grades. If when you collect your A level results you have to add up your unit scores to find out your final grades, it means your school or college has not 'cashed in' your results.

We only receive cashed in results from the exam boards, so if your school or college has not cashed in your results, you must ask them to send a 'cash in' request to the exam board. You also need to tell the universities and colleges where you're holding offers that there'll be a delay in receiving your results and call our Customer Service Unit to find out when your results have been received.

When we receive your 'cashed in' results from the exam board we'll send them to the universities and colleges where you're holding offers straight away.

WHAT IF YOU DON'T HAVE A PLACE?

If you have not met the conditions of either your firm or insurance choice, and your chosen universities or colleges have not confirmed your place, you are eligible for Clearing. In Clearing you can apply for courses that still have vacancies. Clearing operates from mid-July to late September 2012 (page 148).

BETTER RESULTS THAN EXPECTED?

If you obtain exam results that meet and exceed the conditions of the offer for your firm choice, you can for a short period use a process called Adjustment to look for an alternative place, whilst still keeping your original firm choice. See page 151 for information about Adjustment.

Next steps

5

Step 5 – Next steps

You might find yourself with different exam results than you were expecting, or you may change your mind about what you want to do. If so, there may be other options open to you.

CLEARING

Clearing is a service that helps people without a place find suitable course vacancies. It runs from mid-July until the end of September, but most people use it after the exam results are published in August.

You could consider related or alternative subjects or perhaps combining your original choice of subject with another. Your teachers or careers adviser, or the universities and colleges themselves, can provide useful guidance.

Course vacancies are listed at **www.ucas.com** and in the national media following the publication of exam results in August. Once you have your exam results, if you're in Clearing you need to look at the vacancy listings and then contact any university or college you are interested in.

Talk to the institutions; don't be afraid to call them. Make sure you have your Personal ID and Clearing Number ready and prepare notes on what you will say to them about:

- why you want to study the course
- why you want to study at their university or college
- any relevant employment or activities you have done that relate to the course
- your grades.

Accepting an offer - you can contact as many universities and colleges as you like through Clearing, and you may informally be offered more than one place. If this happens, you will need to decide which offer you want to accept. If you're offered a place you want to be formally considered for, you enter the course details in Track, and the university or college will then let you know if they're accepting you.

ADJUSTMENT

If you receive better results than expected, and meet and exceed the conditions of your conditional firm choice, you have the opportunity to reconsider what and where you want to study. This process is called Adjustment.

Adjustment runs from A level results day on 16 August 2012 until the end of August. Your individual Adjustment period starts on A level results day or when your conditional firm choice changes to unconditional firm, whichever is the later. You then have a maximum of five calendar days to register and secure an alternative course, if you decide you want to do this. If you want to try to find an alternative course you must register in Track to use Adjustment, so universities and colleges can view your application.

There are no vacancy listings for Adjustment, so you'll need to talk to the institutions. When you contact a university or college make it clear that you are applying through Adjustment, not Clearing. If they want to consider you they will ask for your Personal ID, so they can view your application.

If you don't find an alternative place then you remain accepted at your original firm choice.

Adjustment is entirely optional; remember that nothing really beats the careful research you carried out to find the right courses before you made your UCAS

application. Talk to a careers adviser at your school, college or local careers office, as they can help you decide if registering to use Adjustment is right for you.

More information about Adjustment and Clearing is available at **www.ucas.com**. You can also view UCAStv video guides on how to use Adjustment and Clearing at **www.ucas.tv**.

IF YOU ARE STILL WITHOUT A PLACE TO STUDY

If you haven't found a suitable place, or changed your mind about what you want to do, there are lots of other options. Ask for advice from your school, college or careers office. Here are some suggestions you might want to consider:

- studying a part-time course (there's a part-time course search at www.ucas.com from July until September)
- studying a foundation degree
- re-sit your exams
- getting some work experience
- studying in another country
- reapplying next year to university or college through UCAS
- taking a gap year
- doing an apprenticeship (you'll find a vacancy search on the National Apprenticeship Service (NAS) website at **www.apprenticeships.org.uk**)
- finding a job
- starting a business.

More advice and links to other organisations can be found on the UCAS website at **www.ucas.com/students/nextsteps/advice**.

IF YOU ARE STILL WITHOUT A PLACE TO STUDY:

You could re-sit your exams and try again next year, find employment, decide to do a further education course or apply for a part-time course and a part-time job. Seek advice from your school or college or careers office.

Starting university
or college

Step 6 – Starting university or college

Congratulations! Now you have your place at university or college you will need to finalise your plans on how to get there, where to live and how to finance it. Make lists of things to do and people whose help you can call on. Will you have to travel independently or can your parents or relatives help with transport? If you are keeping a car at uni, have you checked out parking facilities and told your insurance company?

Make sure you have everything organised, including travel arrangements, essential documents and paperwork, books and equipment required for the course. The university will send you joining information – contact the Admissions Office or the Students' Union if you have questions about anything to do with starting your course.

Where to live - unless you are planning to live at home, your university or college will usually provide you with guidance on how to find somewhere to live. The earlier you contact them the better your chance of finding a suitable range of options, from hall to private landlords, to choose from. Find out what facilities are available at the different accommodation options. Check what you need to bring with you and what is supplied. Don't leave it all to the last minute – especially things like arranging a bank account, checking what proof of identity you might need, gathering together a few essentials like supplies of coffee, insurance cover, TV licence etc.

Student finance - you will need to budget for living costs, accommodation, travel, books and tuition fees. Learn about budgeting by visiting **www.ucas**.com where you will find further links to useful resources to help you manage your money. Remember that if you do get into financial difficulties the Welfare Office at the university will help you change tack and manage better in future, but it is always better to live within your means from the outset.

www.yougofurther.co.uk - the UCAS student network allows you to make friends with other students who are going to the same university or college and could be on the same course. yougo allows you to talk to UCAS online as well as to the universities and colleges on their profile pages. yougo is your direct route to the information you need.

Useful contacts

CONNECTING WITH UCAS

You can follow UCAS on Twitter at **www.twitter.com/ucas_online**, and ask a question or see what others are asking on Facebook at **www.facebook.com/ucasonline**. You can also watch videos of UCAS advisers answering frequently asked questions on YouTube at **www.youtube.com/ucasonline**.

There are many UCAStv video guides to help with your journey into higher education, such as *How to choose your courses*, Attending events, and How to apply. These can all be viewed at **www.ucas.tv** or in the relevant section of **www.ucas.com**.

If you need to speak to UCAS, please contact the Customer Service Unit on 0871 468 0 468 or 0044 871 468 0 468 from outside the UK. Calls from BT landlines within the UK will cost no more than 9p per minute. The cost of calls from mobiles and other networks may vary.

If you have hearing difficulties, you can call the Text Relay service on 18001 0871 468 0 468 (outside the UK 0044 151 494 1260). Calls are charged at normal rates.

www.yougofurther.co.uk: 'yougo', as it is more commonly known, is the UCAS student network. On yougo you can make friends with other applicants who are going to the same university or college and/or who are going to be on the same course.

CAREERS ADVICE

Connexions Direct is for you if you live in England, are aged 13 to 19 and want advice on getting to where you want to be in life.

Connexions personal advisers can give you information, advice and practical help with all sorts of things, like choosing subjects at school or mapping out your future career options. They can help you with anything that might be affecting you at school, college, work or in your personal or family life.

Contact a Connexions Direct adviser at **www.direct.gov.uk/en/youngpeople/index.htm**.

Careers Scotland provides a starting point for anyone looking for careers information, advice or guidance. **www.careers-scotland.org.uk**.

Careers Wales – Wales' national all-age careers guidance service.
www.careerswales.com or **www.gyrfacymru.com**.

Northern Ireland Careers Service website for the new, all-age careers guidance service in Northern Ireland. **www.careersserviceni.com**. Learndirect – Not sure what job you want? Need help to decide which course to do? Give learndirect a call on 0800 101 901 or, for Scotland, 0808 100 9000.
www.learndirect.co.uk.
www.learndirectscotland.com.

GENERAL HIGHER EDUCATION ADVICE

Unistats at **www.direct.gov.uk/unistats** is the official website to help you make an informed choice when deciding which UK university or college to apply to. It includes the results of the latest National Student Survey.

National Union of Students (NUS) is the national voice of students, helping them to campaign, get cheap student discounts and provide advice on living student life to the full - **www.nus.org.uk**.

STUDENTS WITH DISABILITIES

If you have a disability or specific learning difficulty, you are strongly encouraged to make early direct contact with individual institutions before submitting your application. Most universities and colleges have disability coordinators or advisers. You can find their contact details and further advice at the Skill: National Bureau for Students with Disabilities' website – **www.skill.org.uk**.

There is financial help for students with disabilities, known as Disabled Students' Allowances (DSAs). More information is available on the Directgov website at **www.direct.gov.uk/disabledstudents**.

YEAR OUT

For useful information on taking a year out, see **www.gap-year.com**.

The Year Out Group website is packed with information and guidance for young people and their parents and advisers. **www.yearoutgroup.org**.

Essential reading

UCAS has brought together the best books and resources you need to make the important decisions regarding entry to higher education. With guidance on choosing courses, finding the right institution, information about student finance, admissions tests, gap years and lots more, you can find the most trusted guides at **www.ucasbooks.com**.

The publications listed on the following pages and many others are available through **www.ucasbooks.com** or from UCAS Publication Services unless otherwise stated.

UCAS PUBLICATION SERVICES
UCAS Publication Services
PO Box 130, Cheltenham
Gloucestershire GL52 3ZF
f: 01242 544 806
e: publicationservices@ucas.ac.uk
// **www.ucasbooks.com**

ENTIRE RESEARCH AND APPLICATION PROCESS EXPLAINED

The UCAS Guide to getting into University and College
This brand new guide contains advice and information about the entire research and application process, and brings together the expertise of UCAS staff, along with insights and tips from well known universities including Oxford and Cambridge, and students who are involved with or have experienced the process first-hand.

The book clearly sets out the information you need in an easy-to-read format, with myth busters, tips from students, checklists and much more; this book will be a companion for applicants throughout their entire journey into higher education.
Published by UCAS
Price: £11.99

NEED HELP COMPLETING YOUR APPLICATION?

How to Complete your UCAS Application 2012
A must for anyone applying through UCAS. Contains advice on the preparation needed, a step-by-step guide to filling out the UCAS application, information on the UCAS process and useful tips for completing the personal statement.
Published by Trotman
Price £12.99

Insider's Guide to Applying to University
Full of honest insights, this is a thorough guide to the application process. It reveals advice from careers advisers and current students, guidance on making sense of university information and choosing courses. Also includes tips for the personal statement, interviews, admissions tests, UCAS Extra and Clearing.
Published by Trotman
Price £12.99

How to Write a Winning UCAS Personal Statement
The personal statement is your chance to stand out from the crowd. Based on information from admissions tutors, this book will help you sell yourself. It includes specific guidance for over 30 popular subjects, common mistakes to avoid, information on what admissions tutors look for, and much more.
Published by Trotman
Price £12.99

CHOOSING COURSES

Progression Series 2012 entry
The 'Progression to…' titles are designed to help you access good quality, useful information on some of the most competitive subject areas. The books cover advice on applying through UCAS, routes to qualifications, course details, job prospects, case studies and career advice.

Progression to…
Art and Design
Economics, Finance and Accountancy
Engineering and Mathematics
Journalism, Broadcasting, Media Production and Performing Arts
Law
Medicine, Dentistry and Optometry
Nursing, Healthcare and Social Work
Psychology
Sports Science and Physiotherapy
Teaching and Education
Published by UCAS
Price £15.99 each

UCAS Parent Guide
Free of charge.
Order online at **www.ucas.com/parents**.

Open Days 2011
Attending open days, taster courses and higher education conventions is an important part of the application process. This publication makes planning attendance at these events quick and easy.
Published annually by UCAS.
Price £3.50

ESSENTIAL READING

'Getting into…' guides

Clear and concise guides to help applicants secure places. They include qualifications required, advice on applying, tests, interviews and case studies. The guides give an honest view and discuss current issues and careers.

Getting into Business and Economics
Getting into Veterinary School
Getting into Oxford and Cambridge
Published by Trotman
Price £12.99 each

Choosing Your Degree Course & University

With so many universities and courses to choose from, it is not an easy decision for students embarking on their journey to higher education. This guide will offer expert guidance on the questions students need to ask when considering the opportunities available.
Published by Trotman
Price £24.99

Degree Course Descriptions

Providing details of the nature of degree courses, the descriptions in this book are written by heads of departments and senior lecturers at major universities. Each description contains an overview of the course area, details of course structures, career opportunities and more.
Published by COA
Price £12.99

CHOOSING WHERE TO STUDY

The Virgin Guide to British Universities

An insider's guide to choosing a university or college. Written by students and using independent statistics, this guide evaluates what you get from a higher education institution.
Published by Virgin
Price £16.99

Times Good University Guide 2012

How do you find the best university for the subject you wish to study? You need a guide that evaluates the quality of what is available, giving facts, figures and comparative assessments of universities. The rankings provide hard data, analysed, interpreted and presented by a team of experts.
Published by Harper Collins
Price £16.99

Which Uni?

One person's perfect uni might be hell for someone else. Picking the right one will give you the best chance of future happiness, academic success and brighter job prospects. This guide is packed with tables from a variety of sources, rating universities on everything from the quality of teaching to the make-up of the student population and much more.
Published by Trotman
Price £14.99

Getting into the UK's Best Universities and Courses

This book is for those who set their goals high and dream of studying on a highly regarded course at a good university. It provides information on selecting the best courses for a subject, the application and personal statement, interviews, results day, timescales for applications and much more.
Published by Trotman
Price £12.99

FINANCIAL INFORMATION

Student Finance

All students need to know about tuition fees, loans, grants, bursaries and much more. Covering all forms of income and expenditure, this comprehensive guide is produced in association with UCAS and offers great value for money.
Published by Constable Robinson
Price: £7.99

The Essential Guide to Paying for University

Parents and students alike are increasingly concerned about the rising cost of university education. However, there are strategies that can help, and there are many bursaries that go unclaimed every year. This guide covers the cost of university, funding available to help, and how parents and students can plan and budget.
Published by Kogan Page
Price £9.99

University Scholarships, Awards & Bursaries

Students embarking on HE courses face an increasingly challenging financial situation. This book enables applicants and current students to find the support that may help them make ends meet. Packed with information on virtually all awards available.
Published by Trotman
Price £22.99

CAREERS PLANNING

A-Z of Careers and Jobs

It is vital to be well informed about career decisions and this guide will help you make the right choice. It provides full details of the wide range of opportunities on the market, the personal qualities and skills needed for each job, entry qualifications and training, realistic salary expectations and useful contact details.
Published by Kogan Page
Price £16.99

The Careers Directory

An indispensable resource for anyone seeking careers information, covering over 350 careers. It presents up-to-date information in an innovative double-page format. Ideal for students in years 10 to 13 who are considering their futures and for other careers professionals.
Published by COA
Price £14.99

Careers with a Science Degree

Over 100 jobs and areas of work for graduates of biological, chemical and physical sciences are described in this guide. Whether you have yet to choose your degree subject and want to know where the various choices could lead, or are struggling for ideas about what to do with your science degree, this book will guide and inspire you. The title includes: nature of the work and potential employers, qualifications required for entry, including personal qualities and skills; training routes and opportunities for career development and postgraduate study options.
Published by Lifetime Publishing
Price: £12.99

Careers with an Arts and Humanities Degree

Covers careers and graduate opportunities related to these degrees. The book describes over 100 jobs and areas of work suitable for graduates from a range of disciplines including: English and modern languages, history and geography, music and the fine arts. The guide highlights: graduate opportunities, training routes, postgraduate study options and entry requirements.
Published by Lifetime Publishing
Price: £12.99

DEFERRING ENTRY

Your Gap Year

The essential book for all young people planning a gap year before continuing with their education. This up-to-date guide provides essential information on specialist gap year programmes, as well as the vast range of jobs and voluntary opportunities available to young people around the world.
Published by Crimson Publishing
Price £12.99

Gap Year Guidebook 2011

This thorough and easy-to-use guide contains everything you need to know before taking a gap year. It includes real-life traveller tips, hundreds of contact details, realistic advice on everything from preparing, learning and working abroad, coping with coming home and much more.
Published by John Catt Education
Price £14.99

Summer Jobs Worldwide 2011

This unique and specialist guide contains over 40,000 jobs for all ages. No other book includes such a variety and wealth of summer work opportunities in Britain and aboard. Anything from horse trainer in Iceland, to a guide for nature walks in Peru, to a yoga centre helper in Greece, to an animal keeper for London Zoo, can be found.
Published by Crimson Publishing
Price £14.99

Please note all publications incur a postage and packing charge. All information was correct at the time of printing.

For a full list of publications, please visit
www.ucasbooks.com.

Courses

Courses

Keen to get started on your medicine, optometry-related or dentistry career? This section contains details of the various degree courses available at UK institutions.

EXPLAINING THE LIST OF COURSES

The list of courses has been divided into subject categories (see over for list of subjects). We list the universities and colleges by their UCAS institution codes. Within each institution, courses are listed first by award type (such as BA, BSc, FdA, HND, MA and many others), then alphabetically by course title.

You might find some courses showing an award type '(Mod)', which indicates a combined degree that might be modular in design. A small number of courses have award type '(FYr)'. This indicates a 12-month foundation course, after which students can choose to apply for a degree course. In either case, you should contact the university or college for further details.

Generally speaking, when a course comprises two or more subjects, the word used to connect the subjects indicates the make-up of the award: 'Subject A and Subject B' is a joint award, where both subjects carry equal weight; 'Subject A with Subject B' is a major/minor award, where Subject A accounts for at least 60% of your study. If the title shows 'Subject A/Subject B', it may indicate that students can decide on the weighting of the subjects at the end of the first year. You should check with the university or college for full details.

Each entry in the UCAS sections shows the UCAS course code and the duration of the course. Where known, the entry contains details of the minimum qualification requirements for the course, as supplied to UCAS by the universities and colleges. Bear in mind that possessing the minimum qualifications does not guarantee acceptance to the course: there may be far more applicants than places. You may be asked to attend an interview.

Courses with entry requirements that require applicants to disclose information about spent and unspent convictions and may require a Criminal Records Bureau (CRB) check, are marked '**CRB Check:** Required'.

Before applying for any course, you are advised to contact the university or college to check any changes in entry requirements and to see if any new courses have come on stream since the lists were approved for publication. To make this easy, each institution's entry starts with their address, email, phone and fax details, as well as their website address. You will also find it useful to check the Entry Profiles section of Course Search at **www.ucas.com**.

LIST OF SUBJECT CATEGORIES

The list of courses in this section has been divided into the following subject categories.

MEDICINE

A20 THE UNIVERSITY OF ABERDEEN
UNIVERSITY OFFICE
KING'S COLLEGE
ABERDEEN AB24 3FX
t: +44 (0) 1224 273504 f: +44 (0) 1224 272034
e: sras@abdn.ac.uk
// www.abdn.ac.uk/sras

A100 MB Medicine
Duration: 5FT Hon   CRB Check: Required
Entry Requirements: *GCE:* AAA. *SQAH:* AAAAB. *SQAAH:* ABB. *IB:*
36. Interview required. Admissions Test required.

B32 THE UNIVERSITY OF BIRMINGHAM
EDGBASTON
BIRMINGHAM B15 2TT
t: 0121 415 8900 f: 0121 414 7159
e: admissions@bham.ac.uk
// www.bham.ac.uk

A100 MBChB Medicine (5 years)
Duration: 5FT Hon   CRB Check: Required
Entry Requirements: *GCE:* A*AA-AAA. *SQAH:* AAAAB-AAABB.
SQAAH: AAA-AAB. *IB:* 36. Interview required.

A101 MBChB Medicine (Graduate Entry) (4 years)
Duration: 4FT Hon   CRB Check: Required
Entry Requirements: Interview required.

B74 BRIGHTON AND SUSSEX MEDICAL SCHOOL
UNIVERSITY OF BRIGHTON
THE CHECKLAND BUILDING
FALMER
BRIGHTON BN1 9PH
t: 01273 643528 f: 01273 643970
e: medadmissions@bsms.ac.uk
// www.bsms.ac.uk

A100 BMBS Medicine
Duration: 5FT Hon   CRB Check: Required
Entry Requirements: *GCE:* A*AB-AAA. *IB:* 38. Interview required.
Admissions Test required.

B78 UNIVERSITY OF BRISTOL
UNDERGRADUATE ADMISSIONS OFFICE
SENATE HOUSE
TYNDALL AVENUE
BRISTOL BS8 1TH
t: 0117 928 9000 f: 0117 925 1424
e: ug-admissions@bristol.ac.uk
// www.bristol.ac.uk

A104 MB Medicine - MBChB Pre-medical entry (6 years)
Duration: 6FT Hon   CRB Check: Required
Entry Requirements: *GCE:* A*AB-AAA. *SQAH:* AAAAA. *SQAAH:* AA.
IB: 37. *BTEC ND:* DDD. Interview required.

A100 MB Medicine - MBChB Standard entry (5 years)
Duration: 5FT Hon   CRB Check: Required
Entry Requirements: *GCE:* A*AB-AAA. *SQAH:* AAAAA. *SQAAH:* AA.
IB: 37. *BTEC ND:* DDD. Interview required.

A101 MBChB Medicine - MBChB Graduate entry (4 years)
Duration: 4FT Hon   CRB Check: Required
Entry Requirements: *GCE:* ABC-BBB. *SQAH:* BBBBB. *SQAAH:* BB.
IB: 32. Interview required.

C05 UNIVERSITY OF CAMBRIDGE
CAMBRIDGE ADMISSIONS OFFICE
FITZWILLIAM HOUSE
32 TRUMPINGTON STREET
CAMBRIDGE CB2 1QY
t: 01223 333 308 f: 01223 746 868
e: admissions@cam.ac.uk
// www.cam.ac.uk/admissions/undergraduate/

A101 MB Cambridge Graduate Course in Medicine
Duration: 4FT Hon   CRB Check: Required
Entry Requirements: *GCE:* A*AA. *SQAAH:* AAA-AAB. Interview required.

A100 MB Medicine
Duration: 6FT Hon   CRB Check: Required
Entry Requirements: *GCE:* A*AA. *SQAAH:* AAA-AAB. Interview required. Admissions Test required.

C15 CARDIFF UNIVERSITY
PO BOX 927
30-36 NEWPORT ROAD
CARDIFF CF24 0DE
t: 029 2087 9999 f: 029 2087 6138
e: admissions@cardiff.ac.uk
// www.cardiff.ac.uk

A100 MBBCh Medicine (first-year entry)
Duration: 5FT Hon CRB Check: Required
Entry Requirements: *GCE:* AAA. *IB:* 36. Interview required.
Admissions Test required.

A104 MBBCh Medicine (foundation course)
Duration: 6FT Hon CRB Check: Required
Entry Requirements: *GCE:* AAA. *SQAH:* AAAAB. *IB:* 36. *BTEC ND:*
DDD. Interview required. Admissions Test required.

D65 UNIVERSITY OF DUNDEE
NETHERGATE
DUNDEE DD1 4HN
t: 01382 383838 f: 01382 388150
e: contactus@dundee.ac.uk
// www.dundee.ac.uk/admissions/
undergraduate/

A100 MB Medicine
Duration: 5FT Hon CRB Check: Required
Entry Requirements: *GCE:* AAA. *SQAH:* AAABB. *IB:* 37. Interview
required. Admissions Test required.

A104 MB Medicine (Pre-medical year)
Duration: 6FT Hon CRB Check: Required
Entry Requirements: *GCE:* AAA. *SQAH:* AAAAB. *IB:* 37. Interview
required. Admissions Test required.

D86 DURHAM UNIVERSITY
DURHAM UNIVERSITY
UNIVERSITY OFFICE
DURHAM DH1 3HP
t: 0191 334 2000 f: 0191 334 6055
e: admissions@durham.ac.uk
// www.durham.ac.uk

A190 FYr Gateway to Medicine
Duration: 1FT FYr
Entry Requirements: Contact the institution for details.

E14 UNIVERSITY OF EAST ANGLIA
NORWICH NR4 7TJ
t: 01603 591515 f: 01603 458596
e: admissions@uea.ac.uk
// www.uea.ac.uk

A100 MBBS Medicine
Duration: 5FT Hon CRB Check: Required
Entry Requirements: *GCE:* AAAb. *IB:* 34. Interview required.
Admissions Test required.

A104 MBBS Medicine with a Foundation Year
Duration: 6FT Hon CRB Check: Required
Entry Requirements: *GCE:* BBB. *SQAH:* BBBBBB. *SQAAH:* BBB. *IB:*
31. *BTEC ND:* DDM. Interview required. Admissions Test required.

E56 THE UNIVERSITY OF EDINBURGH
STUDENT RECRUITMENT & ADMISSIONS
57 GEORGE SQUARE
EDINBURGH EH8 9JU
t: 0131 650 4360 f: 0131 651 1236
e: sra.enquiries@ed.ac.uk
// www.ed.ac.uk/studying/undergraduate/

A100 MBChB Medicine
Duration: 5FT Hon CRB Check: Required
Entry Requirements: *GCE:* AAAb. *SQAH:* AAAAB. *IB:* 37.
Admissions Test required.

G28 UNIVERSITY OF GLASGOW
THE UNIVERSITY OF GLASGOW
THE FRASER BUILDING
65 HILLHEAD STREET
GLASGOW G12 8QF
t: 0141 330 6062 f: 0141 330 2961
e: student.recruitment@glasgow.ac.uk
// www.glasgow.ac.uk

A100 MB Medicine
Duration: 5FT Hon CRB Check: Required
Entry Requirements: *GCE:* AAA. *SQAH:* AAAAB. *IB:* 36.
Admissions Test required.

G42 GLASGOW CALEDONIAN UNIVERSITY
STUDENT RECRUITMENT & ADMISSIONS SERVICE
CITY CAMPUS
COWCADDENS ROAD
GLASGOW G4 0BA
t: 0141 331 3000 f: 0141 331 8676
e: undergraduate@gcu.ac.uk
// www.gcu.ac.uk

A990 BSc Oral Health Science
Duration: 3FT Ord   CRB Check: Required
Entry Requirements: *GCE:* CCC. *SQAH:* BBBB. *IB:* 28. Interview required.

H75 HULL YORK MEDICAL SCHOOL
HYMS ADMISSIONS SECTION
ADMISSIONS AND UK/EU STUDENT RECRUITMENT
UNIVERSITY OF YORK
HESLINGTON, YORK YO10 5DD
t: 0870 120 2323 f: 01904 433538
e: admissions@hyms.ac.uk
// www.hyms.ac.uk

A100 MBBS Medicine
Duration: 5FT Hon   CRB Check: Required
Entry Requirements: *GCE:* AAAb. *SQAH:* AAAAB. *SQAAH:* AA. *IB:* 36. Interview required. Admissions Test required.

I50 IMPERIAL COLLEGE LONDON
REGISTRY
SOUTH KENSINGTON CAMPUS
IMPERIAL COLLEGE LONDON
LONDON SW7 2AZ
t: 020 7589 5111 f: 020 7594 8004
// www.imperial.ac.uk

A101 MBBS Medicine (Graduate Entry)
Duration: 4FT Hon   CRB Check: Required
Entry Requirements: Interview required. Admissions Test required.

A100 MBBS/BSc Medicine
Duration: 6FT Hon   CRB Check: Required
Entry Requirements: *GCE:* AAAb. *SQAAH:* AAA. *IB:* 38. Interview required. Admissions Test required.

K12 KEELE UNIVERSITY
STAFFS ST5 5BG
t: 01782 734005 f: 01782 632343
e: undergraduate@keele.ac.uk
// www.keele.ac.uk

A100 MBChB Medicine
Duration: 5FT Hon   CRB Check: Required
Entry Requirements: *GCE:* AAB. *SQAAH:* AAB. *IB:* 34. Interview required. Admissions Test required.

A101 MBChB Medicine (Graduate Entry)
Duration: 4FT Hon   CRB Check: Required
Entry Requirements: Admissions Test required.

A104 MBChB Medicine with Health Foundation Year
Duration: 6FT Hon   CRB Check: Required
Entry Requirements: *GCE:* AAB. *SQAAH:* AAB. *IB:* 34. *BTEC ND:* DDD. Admissions Test required.

K60 KING'S COLLEGE LONDON (UNIVERSITY OF LONDON)
STRAND
LONDON WC2R 2LS
t: 020 7848 7070 f: 020 7848 7171
e: prospective@kcl.ac.uk
// www.kcl.ac.uk

A100 MBBS Medicine (5 years)
Duration: 5FT Hon   CRB Check: Required
Entry Requirements: *GCE:* AAAb. *SQAH:* BBB. *SQAAH:* AA. *IB:* 38. Interview required. Admissions Test required.

A102 MBBS Medicine Graduate/Professional Entry Programme (4 years)
Duration: 4FT Hon   CRB Check: Required
Entry Requirements: Interview required. Admissions Test required.

A104 MBBS Medicine Maxfax Entry Programme (MFDS candidates only/4 years)
Duration: 4FT Hon   CRB Check: Required
Entry Requirements: Interview required.

A101 MBBS6 Extended Medical Degree Programme (6 years)
Duration: 6FT Hon   CRB Check: Required
Entry Requirements: *GCE:* BBC-BCC. Interview required. Admissions Test required.

L14 LANCASTER UNIVERSITY
THE UNIVERSITY
LANCASTER
LANCASHIRE LA1 4YW
t: 01524 592029 f: 01524 846243
e: ugadmissions@lancaster.ac.uk
// www.lancs.ac.uk

A900 CertHE Pre-Medical Studies
Duration: 1FT Cer
Entry Requirements: *GCE:* ABB. *SQAH:* BBBBB. *SQAAH:* BBB.

L23 UNIVERSITY OF LEEDS
THE UNIVERSITY OF LEEDS
WOODHOUSE LANE
LEEDS LS2 9JT
t: 0113 343 3999
e: admissions@leeds.ac.uk
// www.leeds.ac.uk

A100 MBChB Medicine
Duration: 5FT Hon   CRB Check: Required
Entry Requirements: *GCE:* AAA. *SQAH:* AAAAB. *SQAAH:* AAB. *IB:* 36. Admissions Test required.

L34 UNIVERSITY OF LEICESTER
UNIVERSITY ROAD
LEICESTER LE1 7RH
t: 0116 252 5281 f: 0116 252 2447
e: admissions@le.ac.uk
// www.le.ac.uk

A100 MBChB Medicine
Duration: 5FT Hon   CRB Check: Required
Entry Requirements: *GCE:* AAA. *SQAH:* AAAAA. *SQAAH:* AAA. *IB:* 36. *BTEC ND:* DDD. Interview required. Admissions Test required.

A101 MBChB Medicine (Graduate Entry)
Duration: 4FT Hon   CRB Check: Required
Entry Requirements: Interview required. Admissions Test required.

L41 THE UNIVERSITY OF LIVERPOOL
THE FOUNDATION BUILDING
BROWNLOW HILL
LIVERPOOL L69 7ZX
t: 0151 794 2000 f: 0151 708 6502
e: ugrecruitment@liv.ac.uk
// www.liv.ac.uk

A100 MBChB Medicine
Duration: 5FT Hon   CRB Check: Required
Entry Requirements: *GCE:* AAAb. *SQAH:* AAAAA-AAAAB. *SQAAH:* AA. *IB:* 36. Interview required.

A101 MBChB Medicine (Graduate Entry)
Duration: 4FT Hon   CRB Check: Required
Entry Requirements: *IB:* 32. Interview required.

A105 MBChB Medicine (based at Lancaster University)
Duration: 5FT Hon   CRB Check: Required
Entry Requirements: *IB:* 36. Interview required.

M20 THE UNIVERSITY OF MANCHESTER
OXFORD ROAD
MANCHESTER M13 9PL
t: 0161 275 2077 f: 0161 275 2106
e: ug-admissions@manchester.ac.uk
// www.manchester.ac.uk

A106 MBChB Medicine
Duration: 5FT Hon   CRB Check: Required
Entry Requirements: *GCE:* AAA. *SQAAH:* AAA. *IB:* 37. Interview required. Admissions Test required.

A104 MBChB Medicine (6 years including foundation year)
Duration: 6FT Hon   CRB Check: Required
Entry Requirements: *GCE:* ABB. *SQAH:* AAABB. *SQAAH:* ABB. *IB:* 33. Interview required. Admissions Test required.

M80 MIDDLESEX UNIVERSITY
MIDDLESEX UNIVERSITY
THE BURROUGHS
LONDON NW4 4BT
t: 020 8411 5555 f: 020 8411 5649
e: enquiries@mdx.ac.uk
// www.mdx.ac.uk

A900 MCM Ayurvedic Medicine
Duration: 4FT Oth
Entry Requirements: Contact the institution for details.

N21 NEWCASTLE UNIVERSITY
KING'S GATE
NEWCASTLE UPON TYNE NE1 7RU
t: 0191 208 3333 f: 0191 222 6143
// www.ncl.ac.uk

A101 MBBS Medicine (Accelerated Programme, Graduate Entry)
Duration: 4FT Hon   CRB Check: Required
Entry Requirements: Interview required. Admissions Test required.

A100 MBBS Medicine (stage 1 entry)
Duration: 5FT Hon   CRB Check: Required
Entry Requirements: *GCE:* AAA. *SQAH:* AAAAA. *IB:* 38. Interview required. Admissions Test required.

N84 THE UNIVERSITY OF NOTTINGHAM
THE ADMISSIONS OFFICE
THE UNIVERSITY OF NOTTINGHAM
UNIVERSITY PARK
NOTTINGHAM NG7 2RD
t: 0115 951 5151 f: 0115 951 4668
// www.nottingham.ac.uk

A100 BMBS Medicine
Duration: 5FT Hon   CRB Check: Required
Entry Requirements: *GCE:* AAA. *SQAAH:* AAB. *IB:* 38.   Interview required. Admissions Test required.

A101 BMBS Medicine (Graduate Entry)
Duration: 4FT Hon   CRB Check: Required
Entry Requirements: Interview required. Admissions Test required.

O33 OXFORD UNIVERSITY
UNDERGRADUATE ADMISSIONS OFFICE
UNIVERSITY OF OXFORD
WELLINGTON SQUARE
OXFORD OX1 2JD
t: 01865 288000 f: 01865 270212
e: undergraduate.admissions@admin.ox.ac.uk
// www.admissions.ox.ac.uk

A100 BMBCh Medicine
Duration: 6FT Hon   CRB Check: Required
Entry Requirements: *GCE:* AAA. *SQAH:* AAAAA. *SQAAH:* AAB.
Interview required. Admissions Test required.

A101 BMBCh4 Medicine (Fast-track, Graduate Entry only)
Duration: 4FT Hon   CRB Check: Required
Entry Requirements: *GCE:* AAA. Interview required. Admissions Test required.

P37 PENINSULA COLLEGE OF MEDICINE & DENTISTRY
THE JOHN BULL BUILDING
TAMAR SCIENCE PARK, RESEARCH WAY
PLYMOUTH PL6 8BU
t: 01752 437333 f: 01752 517842
e: pcmd-admissions@pcmd.ac.uk
// www.pcmd.ac.uk

A100 BMBS Medicine
Duration: 5FT Hon   CRB Check: Required
Entry Requirements: *GCE:* A*AA-AAA. *SQAAH:* AAA. *IB:* 38.
Interview required. Admissions Test required.

Q50 QUEEN MARY, UNIVERSITY OF LONDON
QUEEN MARY, UNIVERSITY OF LONDON
MILE END ROAD
LONDON E1 4NS
t: 020 7882 5555 f: 020 7882 5500
e: admissions@qmul.ac.uk
// www.qmul.ac.uk

A900 DipHE Dental Hygiene and Dental Therapy
Duration: 2.5FT Dip
Entry Requirements: Contact the institution for details.

A100 MBBS Medicine
Duration: 5FT Hon   CRB Check: Required
Entry Requirements: *GCE:* AAAb. *SQAH:* AAA. *SQAAH:* AB. *IB:* 36.
Admissions Test required.

A101 MBBS Medicine (Graduate Entry)
Duration: 4FT Hon   CRB Check: Required
Entry Requirements: Admissions Test required.

Q75 QUEEN'S UNIVERSITY BELFAST
UNIVERSITY ROAD
BELFAST BT7 1NN
t: 028 9097 3838 f: 028 9097 5151
e: admissions@qub.ac.uk
// www.qub.ac.uk

A100 MB Medicine
Duration: 5FT Hon   CRB Check: Required
Entry Requirements: *GCE:* AAAa. *SQAH:* AAAAA-AAABB. *SQAAH:* AAA-AA. *IB:* 36. Interview required. Admissions Test required.

S18 THE UNIVERSITY OF SHEFFIELD
THE UNIVERSITY OF SHEFFIELD
9 NORTHUMBERLAND ROAD
SHEFFIELD S10 2TT
t: 0114 222 8030 f: 0114 222 8032
// www.sheffield.ac.uk

A104 MBChB Medicine (Foundation Year)
Duration: 6FT Hon   CRB Check: Required
Entry Requirements: *GCE:* AAA. *SQAH:* AAAAB. *SQAAH:* AB. *IB:* 37. *BTEC ND:* DDD. Admissions Test required.

A100 MBChB Medicine (Phase One)
Duration: 5FT Hon   CRB Check: Required
Entry Requirements: *GCE:* AAA. *SQAH:* AAAAB. *SQAAH:* AB. *IB:* 37. *BTEC ND:* DDD. Admissions Test required.

S27 UNIVERSITY OF SOUTHAMPTON
HIGHFIELD
SOUTHAMPTON SO17 1BJ
t: 023 8059 4732 f: 023 8059 3037
e: admissions@soton.ac.uk
// www.southampton.ac.uk

A100 BM Medicine (5 year)
Duration: 5FT Hon   CRB Check: Required
Entry Requirements: *GCE:* AAB. *SQAH:* AAAAB. *SQAAH:* AB. *IB:*
36. Admissions Test required.

A101 BM Medicine - Graduate entry (4 year)
Duration: 4FT Hon   CRB Check: Required
Entry Requirements: Admissions Test required.

A102 BM Medicine - Widening access (6 year) incl Foundation Yr 0
Duration: 6FT Hon   CRB Check: Required
Entry Requirements: *GCE:* AAB. Interview required. Admissions Test required.

S36 UNIVERSITY OF ST ANDREWS
ST KATHARINE'S WEST
16 THE SCORES
ST ANDREWS
FIFE KY16 9AX
t: 01334 462150 f: 01334 463330
e: admissions@st-andrews.ac.uk
// www.st-andrews.ac.uk

A100 MB ChB Medicine
Duration: 6FT Hon   CRB Check: Required
Entry Requirements: *GCE:* AAA. *SQAH:* AAAAB. *IB:* 38. Interview required. Admissions Test required.

A990 MBChB North American Medical Programme
Duration: 6FT Hon   CRB Check: Required
Entry Requirements: Contact the institution for details.

S49 ST GEORGE'S, UNIVERSITY OF LONDON
CRANMER TERRACE
LONDON SW17 0RE
t: +44 (0)20 8725 2333 f: +44 (0)20 8725 0841
e: enquiries@sgul.ac.uk
// www.sgul.ac.uk

A100 MBBS Medicine
Duration: 5FT Hon   CRB Check: Required
Entry Requirements: *GCE:* AAAb-BBCb. *SQAH:* AAAAB. *SQAAH:* AAB. Interview required. Admissions Test required.

A101 MBBS Medicine (Graduate Stream)
Duration: 4FT Hon   CRB Check: Required
Entry Requirements: Interview required. Admissions Test required.

A103 MBBS Medicine (including foundation year)
Duration: 6FT Hon   CRB Check: Required
Entry Requirements: Interview required.

S93 SWANSEA UNIVERSITY
SINGLETON PARK
SWANSEA SA2 8PP
t: 01792 295111 f: 01792 295110
e: admissions@swansea.ac.uk
// www.swansea.ac.uk

A101 MBBCh Medicine (Graduate Entry)
Duration: 4FT Hon   CRB Check: Required
Entry Requirements: Interview required. Admissions Test required.

U80 UNIVERSITY COLLEGE LONDON (UNIVERSITY OF LONDON)
GOWER STREET
LONDON WC1E 6BT
t: 020 7679 3000 f: 020 7679 3001
// www.ucl.ac.uk

A100 MBBS Medicine (6 years)
Duration: 6FT Hon   CRB Check: Required
Entry Requirements: *GCE:* AAAe. *SQAAH:* AAA. *IB:* 38. Interview required. Admissions Test required.

W20 THE UNIVERSITY OF WARWICK
COVENTRY CV4 8UW
t: 024 7652 3723 f: 024 7652 4649
e: ugadmissions@warwick.ac.uk
// www.warwick.ac.uk

A101 MBChB Medicine MBChB - Graduate Entry
Duration: 4FT Hon   CRB Check: Required
Entry Requirements: Interview required. Admissions Test required.

DENTISTRY

A20 THE UNIVERSITY OF ABERDEEN
UNIVERSITY OFFICE
KING'S COLLEGE
ABERDEEN AB24 3FX
t: +44 (0) 1224 273504 f: +44 (0) 1224 272034
e: sras@abdn.ac.uk
// www.abdn.ac.uk/sras

A201 BDS Dental Surgery (Graduates Only)
Duration: 4FT Hon   CRB Check: Required
Entry Requirements: Interview required. Admissions Test required.

B32 THE UNIVERSITY OF BIRMINGHAM
EDGBASTON
BIRMINGHAM B15 2TT
t: 0121 415 8900 f: 0121 414 7159
e: admissions@bham.ac.uk
// www.bham.ac.uk

A200 BDS Dentistry (5 years)
Duration: 5FT Hon   CRB Check: Required
Entry Requirements: *GCE:* AAA. *SQAH:* AAAAB-AAABB. *SQAAH:* AAA-AAB. *IB:* 36. Interview required.

B78 UNIVERSITY OF BRISTOL
UNDERGRADUATE ADMISSIONS OFFICE
SENATE HOUSE
TYNDALL AVENUE
BRISTOL BS8 1TH
t: 0117 928 9000 f: 0117 925 1424
e: ug-admissions@bristol.ac.uk
// www.bristol.ac.uk

A204 BDS Dentistry - First BDS (pre-dental) entry (6 years)
Duration: 6FT Hon   CRB Check: Required
Entry Requirements: *GCE:* AAA. *SQAH:* AAAAA. *SQAAH:* AA. *IB:* 37. *BTEC ND:* DDD. Interview required.

A206 BDS Dentistry - Second BDS entry (5 years)
Duration: 5FT Hon   CRB Check: Required
Entry Requirements: *GCE:* AAA. *SQAH:* AAAAA. *SQAAH:* AA. *IB:* 37. *BTEC ND:* DDD. Interview required.

C15 CARDIFF UNIVERSITY
PO BOX 927
30-36 NEWPORT ROAD
CARDIFF CF24 0DE
t: 029 2087 9999 f: 029 2087 6138
e: admissions@cardiff.ac.uk
// www.cardiff.ac.uk

A200 BDS Dentistry (first year entry)
Duration: 5FT Hon   CRB Check: Required
Entry Requirements: *GCE:* AAA. *IB:* 36. Interview required. Admissions Test required.

A204 BDS Dentistry with Foundation Year
Duration: 6FT Hon   CRB Check: Required
Entry Requirements: *GCE:* AAA. *SQAH:* AABBB. *IB:* 36. *BTEC ND:* DDD. Interview required. Admissions Test required.

C30 UNIVERSITY OF CENTRAL LANCASHIRE
PRESTON
LANCS PR1 2HE
t: 01772 201201 f: 01772 894954
e: uadmissions@uclan.ac.uk
// www.uclan.ac.uk

A202 BDS Dentistry (Graduate Entry)
Duration: 4FT Hon   CRB Check: Required
Entry Requirements: Contact the institution for details.

D65 UNIVERSITY OF DUNDEE
NETHERGATE
DUNDEE DD1 4HN
t: 01382 383838 f: 01382 388150
e: contactus@dundee.ac.uk
// www.dundee.ac.uk/admissions/undergraduate/

A200 BDS Dentistry
Duration: 5FT Hon   CRB Check: Required
Entry Requirements: *GCE:* AAA. *SQAH:* AAAAA. *IB:* 37. Interview required. Admissions Test required.

A204 BDS Dentistry (Pre-dental year)
Duration: 6FT Hon   CRB Check: Required
Entry Requirements: *GCE:* AAA. *SQAH:* AAAAA. *IB:* 37. Interview required. Admissions Test required.

G28 UNIVERSITY OF GLASGOW
THE UNIVERSITY OF GLASGOW
THE FRASER BUILDING
65 HILLHEAD STREET
GLASGOW G12 8QF
t: 0141 330 6062 f: 0141 330 2961
e: student.recruitment@glasgow.ac.uk
// www.glasgow.ac.uk

A200 BDS Dentistry
Duration: 5FT Hon
Entry Requirements: *GCE:* AAB. *SQAH:* AAAAB. *IB:* 36. Interview required. Admissions Test required. Portfolio required.

K60 KING'S COLLEGE LONDON (UNIVERSITY OF LONDON)
STRAND
LONDON WC2R 2LS
t: 020 7848 7070 f: 020 7848 7171
e: prospective@kcl.ac.uk
// www.kcl.ac.uk

A205 BDS Dentistry (5 years)
Duration: 5FT Hon   CRB Check: Required
Entry Requirements: *GCE:* AAAa. *SQAH:* BBB. *SQAAH:* AA. *IB:* 38. Interview required. Admissions Test required.

A204 BDS Dentistry Entry Programme for Medical Graduates
Duration: 3FT Hon   **CRB Check:** Required
Entry Requirements: Interview required.

A202 BDS Dentistry Graduate/Professional Entry Programme (4 years)
Duration: 4FT Hon   **CRB Check:** Required
Entry Requirements: Interview required. Admissions Test required.

L23 UNIVERSITY OF LEEDS
THE UNIVERSITY OF LEEDS
WOODHOUSE LANE
LEEDS LS2 9JT
t: 0113 343 3999
e: admissions@leeds.ac.uk
// www.leeds.ac.uk

A200 MChD Dental Surgery
Duration: 5FT Hon   **CRB Check:** Required
Entry Requirements: *GCE:* AAA. *SQAAH:* AAB. *IB:* 37.

L41 THE UNIVERSITY OF LIVERPOOL
THE FOUNDATION BUILDING
BROWNLOW HILL
LIVERPOOL L69 7ZX
t: 0151 794 2000 f: 0151 708 6502
e: ugrecruitment@liv.ac.uk
// www.liv.ac.uk

A200 BDS Dental Surgery
Duration: 5FT Hon   **CRB Check:** Required
Entry Requirements: *GCE:* AAA. *SQAH:* AAAAA. *SQAAH:* AAA. *IB:* 36. *BTEC ND:* DDD. Interview required.

A201 BDS Dental Surgery (Graduate Entry)
Duration: 4FT Hon   **CRB Check:** Required
Entry Requirements: Interview required.

M20 THE UNIVERSITY OF MANCHESTER
OXFORD ROAD
MANCHESTER M13 9PL
t: 0161 275 2077 f: 0161 275 2106
e: ug-admissions@manchester.ac.uk
// www.manchester.ac.uk

A206 BDS Dentistry (BDS first-year entry)
Duration: 5FT Hon   **CRB Check:** Required
Entry Requirements: *GCE:* AAA. *SQAH:* AAAAB. *SQAAH:* AB. *IB:* 34. Interview required. Admissions Test required.

A204 BDS Dentistry (BDS pre-dental year entry)
Duration: 6FT Hon   **CRB Check:** Required
Entry Requirements: *GCE:* ABB. *SQAH:* AABBB. *SQAAH:* AB. *IB:* 33. Interview required. Admissions Test required.

N21 NEWCASTLE UNIVERSITY
KING'S GATE
NEWCASTLE UPON TYNE NE1 7RU
t: 0191 208 3333 f: 0191 222 6143
// www.ncl.ac.uk

A206 BDS Dentistry
Duration: 5FT Hon   **CRB Check:** Required
Entry Requirements: *GCE:* AAA. *SQAH:* AAAAA. *SQAAH:* AB. *IB:* 35. Interview required. Admissions Test required.

P37 PENINSULA COLLEGE OF MEDICINE & DENTISTRY
THE JOHN BULL BUILDING
TAMAR SCIENCE PARK, RESEARCH WAY
PLYMOUTH PL6 8BU
t: 01752 437333 f: 01752 517842
e: pcmd-admissions@pcmd.ac.uk
// www.pcmd.ac.uk

A201 BDS Dentistry Graduate Entry (4 years)
Duration: 4FT Hon   **CRB Check:** Required
Entry Requirements: Interview required. Admissions Test required.

Q50 QUEEN MARY, UNIVERSITY OF LONDON
QUEEN MARY, UNIVERSITY OF LONDON
MILE END ROAD
LONDON E1 4NS
t: 020 7882 5555 f: 020 7882 5500
e: admissions@qmul.ac.uk
// www.qmul.ac.uk

A200 BDS Dentistry
Duration: 5FT Hon   **CRB Check:** Required
Entry Requirements: *GCE:* AAAb. *SQAH:* AAA. *SQAAH:* AB. *IB:* 36. Admissions Test required.

A201 BDS Dentistry (Graduate Entry)
Duration: 4FT Hon   **CRB Check:** Required
Entry Requirements: Admissions Test required.

Q75 QUEEN'S UNIVERSITY BELFAST
UNIVERSITY ROAD
BELFAST BT7 1NN
t: 028 9097 3838 f: 028 9097 5151
e: admissions@qub.ac.uk
// www.qub.ac.uk

A200 BDS Dentistry
Duration: 5FT Hon   **CRB Check:** Required
Entry Requirements: *GCE:* AAAa. *SQAH:* AAAAA-AAABB. *SQAAH:* AAA-AA. *IB:* 36. Interview required. Admissions Test required.

S18 THE UNIVERSITY OF SHEFFIELD
THE UNIVERSITY OF SHEFFIELD
9 NORTHUMBERLAND ROAD
SHEFFIELD S10 2TT
t: 0114 222 8030 f: 0114 222 8032
// www.sheffield.ac.uk

A200 BDS Dentistry
Duration: 5FT Hon   CRB Check: Required
Entry Requirements: *GCE:* AAA. *SQAH:* AAAAB. *SQAAH:* AA. *IB:*
37. *BTEC ND:* DDD. Interview required. Admissions Test required.

OPTOMETRY

A60 ANGLIA RUSKIN UNIVERSITY
BISHOP HALL LANE
CHELMSFORD
ESSEX CM1 1SQ
t: 0845 271 3333 f: 01245 251789
e: answers@anglia.ac.uk
// www.anglia.ac.uk

B513 BOplo Optometry
Duration: 3FT Hon   CRB Check: Required
Entry Requirements: *GCE:* ABB. *SQAAH:* ABB. *IB:* 30.

B590 BSc Ophthalmic Dispensing
Duration: 3FT Hon   CRB Check: Required
Entry Requirements: *GCE:* 200. *SQAH:* BCCC. *SQAAH:* BB. *IB:* 24.

A80 ASTON UNIVERSITY, BIRMINGHAM
ASTON TRIANGLE
BIRMINGHAM B4 7ET
t: 0121 204 4444 f: 0121 204 3696
e: admissions@aston.ac.uk
// www.aston.ac.uk

B510 BSc Optometry
Duration: 3FT Hon   CRB Check: Required
Entry Requirements: *GCE:* AAA. *SQAH:* AAAAB. *SQAAH:* AAA. *IB:*
34. *BTEC NC:* DD.

B56 THE UNIVERSITY OF BRADFORD
RICHMOND ROAD
BRADFORD
WEST YORKSHIRE BD7 1DP
t: 0800 073 1225 f: 01274 235585
e: course-enquiries@bradford.ac.uk
// www.bradford.ac.uk

B510 BSc Optometry
Duration: 3FT Hon   CRB Check: Required
Entry Requirements: *GCE:* 340. *IB:* 28. Interview required.

B60 BRADFORD COLLEGE: AN ASSOCIATE COLLEGE OF LEEDS METROPOLITAN UNIVERSITY
GREAT HORTON ROAD
BRADFORD
WEST YORKSHIRE BD7 1AY
t: 01274 433008 f: 01274 433185
e: heregistry@bradfordcollege.ac.uk
// www.bradfordcollege.ac.uk/
university-centre

B503 BSc Ophthalmic Dispensing with Management
Duration: 3FT Hon
Entry Requirements: *GCE:* 120-160. *BTEC NC:* DD. *BTEC ND:*
DDD.

C10 CANTERBURY CHRIST CHURCH UNIVERSITY
NORTH HOLMES ROAD
CANTERBURY
KENT CT1 1QU
t: 01227 782900 f: 01227 782888
e: admissions@canterbury.ac.uk
// www.canterbury.ac.uk

B500 BSc Optical Dispensing
Duration: 1FT Hon
Entry Requirements: *GCE:* 240. *IB:* 24.

B501 FdA Optical Dispensing
Duration: 2FT Fdg
Entry Requirements: *GCE:* 120. *IB:* 24.

C15 CARDIFF UNIVERSITY
PO BOX 927
30-36 NEWPORT ROAD
CARDIFF CF24 0DE
t: 029 2087 9999 f: 029 2087 6138
e: admissions@cardiff.ac.uk
// www.cardiff.ac.uk

B510 BSc Optometry
Duration: 3FT Hon   CRB Check: Required
Entry Requirements: *GCE:* AAA. *SQAH:* AAAABB. *SQAAH:* AAB. *IB:*
34. Interview required.

B511 BSc Optometry with a Preliminary Year (4 years)
Duration: 4FT Hon   CRB Check: Required
Entry Requirements: *GCE:* AAA. *SQAH:* AAAABB. *SQAAH:* AAB. *IB:*
34. Interview required.

C60 CITY UNIVERSITY
NORTHAMPTON SQUARE
LONDON EC1V 0HB
t: 020 7040 5060 f: 020 7040 8995
e: ugadmissions@city.ac.uk
// www.city.ac.uk

B512 BSc Advanced Ophthalmic Dispensing (Top-up)
Duration: 1FT Hon
Entry Requirements: Contact the institution for details.

B510 BSc Optometry
Duration: 3FT Hon
Entry Requirements: *GCE:* AAB. *SQAH:* AAAAB. *IB:* 35.

B511 FdSc Ophthalmic Dispensing
Duration: 2FT Fdg
Entry Requirements: *GCE:* 180.

G42 GLASGOW CALEDONIAN UNIVERSITY
STUDENT RECRUITMENT & ADMISSIONS SERVICE
CITY CAMPUS
COWCADDENS ROAD
GLASGOW G4 0BA
t: 0141 331 3000 f: 0141 331 8676
e: undergraduate@gcu.ac.uk
// www.gcu.ac.uk

B502 BSc Ophthalmic Dispensing
Duration: 3FT Deg   CRB Check: Required
Entry Requirements: *GCE:* CC. *SQAH:* BBC. *IB:* 26. *BTEC NC:* MM. *BTEC ND:* MMM.

B510 BSc Optometry
Duration: 4FT Hon   CRB Check: Required
Entry Requirements: *GCE:* AAB. *SQAH:* AAABB. *IB:* 36.

L41 THE UNIVERSITY OF LIVERPOOL
THE FOUNDATION BUILDING
BROWNLOW HILL
LIVERPOOL L69 7ZX
t: 0151 794 2000 f: 0151 708 6502
e: ugrecruitment@liv.ac.uk
// www.liv.ac.uk

B520 BSc Orthoptics
Duration: 3FT Hon   CRB Check: Required
Entry Requirements: *GCE:* BCC. *SQAH:* BBBCC. *SQAAH:* BCC. *IB:* 28. *BTEC ND:* DMM.

M20 THE UNIVERSITY OF MANCHESTER
OXFORD ROAD
MANCHESTER M13 9PL
t: 0161 275 2077 f: 0161 275 2106
e: ug-admissions@manchester.ac.uk
// www.manchester.ac.uk

B510 BSc Optometry
Duration: 3FT Hon   CRB Check: Required
Entry Requirements: *GCE:* AAB. *SQAH:* AAAAB. *SQAAH:* AAB. *IB:* 35. *BTEC ND:* DDD. Interview required.

B511 MOptom Optometry
Duration: 4FT Hon   CRB Check: Required
Entry Requirements: *GCE:* AAB. *SQAH:* AAAAB. *SQAAH:* AAB. *IB:* 35. *BTEC ND:* DDD. Interview required.

P60 UNIVERSITY OF PLYMOUTH
DRAKE CIRCUS
PLYMOUTH PL4 8AA
t: 01752 588037 f: 01752 588050
e: admissions@plymouth.ac.uk
// www.plymouth.ac.uk

B510 BSc Optometry
Duration: 3FT Hon   CRB Check: Required
Entry Requirements: *GCE:* 340. *BTEC NC:* DD. *BTEC ND:* DDD. *OCR ND:* D *OCR NED:* D1

S18 THE UNIVERSITY OF SHEFFIELD
THE UNIVERSITY OF SHEFFIELD
9 NORTHUMBERLAND ROAD
SHEFFIELD S10 2TT
t: 0114 222 8030 f: 0114 222 8032
// www.sheffield.ac.uk

B520 BMS Orthoptics
Duration: 3FT Hon   CRB Check: Required
Entry Requirements: *GCE:* BBB. *SQAH:* BBBBB. *SQAAH:* B. *IB:* 32. *BTEC ND:* DDM. Interview required.

U20 UNIVERSITY OF ULSTER
COLERAINE
CO. LONDONDERRY
NORTHERN IRELAND BT52 1SA
t: 028 7032 4221 f: 028 7032 4908
e: online@ulster.ac.uk
// www.ulster.ac.uk

B510 BSc Optometry
Duration: 3FT Hon   CRB Check: Required
Entry Requirements: *GCE:* AAB. *SQAH:* AAAAB. *SQAAH:* AAB. *IB:* 37. *BTEC NC:* DD. *BTEC ND:* DDD.

W75 UNIVERSITY OF WOLVERHAMPTON
ADMISSIONS UNIT
MX207, CAMP STREET
WOLVERHAMPTON
WEST MIDLANDS WV1 1AD
t: 01902 321000 f: 01902 321896
e: admissions@wlv.ac.uk
// www.wlv.ac.uk

QB15 BA Linguistics and Deaf Studies
Duration: 3FT Hon   CRB Check: Required
Entry Requirements: *GCE:* 160-220. *IB:* 24.

LB45 BA Social Policy and Deaf Studies
Duration: 3FT Hon   CRB Check: Required
Entry Requirements: *GCE:* 160-220. *IB:* 24.

LB55 BA Special Needs & Inclusion Studies and Deaf Studies
Duration: 3FT Hon
Entry Requirements: *GCE:* 160-220. *IB:* 24.

ANATOMY, PHYSIOLOGY AND PATHOLOGY

A20 THE UNIVERSITY OF ABERDEEN
UNIVERSITY OFFICE
KING'S COLLEGE
ABERDEEN AB24 3FX
t: +44 (0) 1224 273504 f: +44 (0) 1224 272034
e: sras@abdn.ac.uk
// www.abdn.ac.uk/sras

B9BC BSc Biomedical Science (Anatomy)
Duration: 4FT Hon
Entry Requirements: *GCE:* ABB. *SQAH:* AABB. *IB:* 32. *BTEC ND:* DDD.

B9B1 BSc Biomedical Science (Physiology)
Duration: 4FT Hon
Entry Requirements: *GCE:* ABB. *SQAH:* AABB. *IB:* 32. *BTEC ND:* DDD.

B170 BSc Neuroscience with Psychology
Duration: 4FT Hon
Entry Requirements: *GCE:* 240. *SQAH:* BBBB. *SQAAH:* BCC. *IB:* 28. *BTEC ND:* MMM.

B120 BSc Physiology
Duration: 4FT Hon
Entry Requirements: *GCE:* 240. *SQAH:* BBBB. *SQAAH:* BCC. *IB:* 28. *BTEC ND:* MMM.

B9BD MSci Biomedical Science (Anatomy) with Industrial Placement
Duration: 5FT Hon
Entry Requirements: *GCE:* ABB. *SQAH:* AABB. *IB:* 32. *BTEC ND:* DDD.

B9BA MSci Biomedical Science (Physiology) with Industrial Placement
Duration: 5FT Hon
Entry Requirements: *GCE:* ABB. *SQAH:* AABB. *IB:* 32. *BTEC ND:* DDD.

B1C8 MSci Neuroscience with Psychology with Industrial Placement
Duration: 5FT Hon
Entry Requirements: *GCE:* ABB. *SQAH:* AABB. *IB:* 32. *BTEC ND:* DDD.

B121 MSci Physiology with Industrial Placement
Duration: 5FT Hon
Entry Requirements: *GCE:* ABB. *SQAH:* AABB. *IB:* 32. *BTEC ND:* DDD.

A60 ANGLIA RUSKIN UNIVERSITY
BISHOP HALL LANE
CHELMSFORD
ESSEX CM1 1SQ
t: 0845 271 3333 f: 01245 251789
e: answers@anglia.ac.uk
// www.anglia.ac.uk

B940 BSc Biomedical Science
Duration: 3FT Hon
Entry Requirements: *GCE:* 200. *SQAH:* BCCC. *SQAAH:* BB. *IB:* 24.

B30 BIRMINGHAM METROPOLITAN COLLEGE (FORMERLY MATTHEW BOULTON COLLEGE)
JENNENS ROAD
BIRMINGHAM B4 7PS
t: 0121 446 4545 f: 0121 503 8590
e: ask@mbc.ac.uk
// www.mbc.ac.uk

B985 BSc Podiatry
Duration: 3FT Hon
Entry Requirements: *GCE:* 220.

V

UCAS

Confused about courses?

Indecisive about institutions?

Stressed about student life?

Unsure about UCAS?

Frowning over finance?

Help is available at
www.ucasbooks.com

B32 THE UNIVERSITY OF BIRMINGHAM
EDGBASTON
BIRMINGHAM B15 2TT
t: 0121 415 8900 f: 0121 414 7159
e: admissions@bham.ac.uk
// www.bham.ac.uk

B160 BSc Physiotherapy
Duration: 3FT Hon   CRB Check: Required
Entry Requirements: *GCE:* AAB. *SQAH:* AAABB-AABBB. *SQAAH:*
AA-AB. *IB:* 34. *BTEC ND:* DDM. Interview required.

BC17 BSc Sport and Exercise Sciences
Duration: 3FT Hon
Entry Requirements: *GCE:* AAA-AAB. *SQAH:* AAAAB-AAABB.
SQAAH: AA. *IB:* 36. *BTEC ND:* DDD.

B50 BOURNEMOUTH UNIVERSITY
TALBOT CAMPUS
FERN BARROW
POOLE
DORSET BH12 5BB
t: 01202 524111
// www.bournemouth.ac.uk

B160 BSc Physiotherapy
Duration: 3FT Hon   CRB Check: Required
Entry Requirements: *GCE:* 340. *IB:* 33. *BTEC ND:* DDD. Interview
required.

B56 THE UNIVERSITY OF BRADFORD
RICHMOND ROAD
BRADFORD
WEST YORKSHIRE BD7 1DP
t: 0800 073 1225 f: 01274 235585
e: course-enquiries@bradford.ac.uk
// www.bradford.ac.uk

H1B1 BEng Medical Engineering
Duration: 3FT Hon
Entry Requirements: *GCE:* 240. *IB:* 24.

H1BC BEng Medical Engineering (4 years)
Duration: 4SW Hon
Entry Requirements: *GCE:* 260. *IB:* 26.

B133 BSc Cancer Biology
Duration: 3FT Hon
Entry Requirements: *GCE:* 260. *IB:* 24. Interview required.

B160 BSc Physiotherapy
Duration: 3FT Hon   CRB Check: Required
Entry Requirements: *GCE:* BBC. *IB:* 30. *BTEC NC:* DM. *BTEC ND:*
DMM. Interview required.

HB11 MEng Medical Engineering
Duration: 4FT Hon
Entry Requirements: *GCE:* 300. *IB:* 26.

HB1C MEng Medical Engineering
Duration: 5SW Hon
Entry Requirements: *GCE:* 300.

B72 UNIVERSITY OF BRIGHTON
209 MITHRAS HOUSE
LEWES ROAD
BRIGHTON BN2 4AT
t: 01273 644644 f: 01273 642607
e: admissions@brighton.ac.uk
// www.brighton.ac.uk

B160 BSc Physiotherapy
Duration: 3FT Hon
Entry Requirements: *GCE:* BBB. *IB:* 32. *BTEC ND:* DDM. Interview
required.

B985 BSc Podiatry
Duration: 3FT Hon
Entry Requirements: *GCE:* BCC. *IB:* 28. Interview required.

B78 UNIVERSITY OF BRISTOL
UNDERGRADUATE ADMISSIONS OFFICE
SENATE HOUSE
TYNDALL AVENUE
BRISTOL BS8 1TH
t: 0117 928 9000 f: 0117 925 1424
e: ug-admissions@bristol.ac.uk
// www.bristol.ac.uk

B131 BSc Cancer Biology and Immunology
Duration: 3FT/4SW Hon
Entry Requirements: *GCE:* ABB. *SQAH:* AABBB. *SQAAH:* AB. *IB:*
33. *BTEC ND:* DDM.

B130 BSc Cellular and Molecular Medicine
Duration: 3FT Hon
Entry Requirements: *GCE:* ABB. *SQAH:* AABBB. *SQAAH:* AB. *IB:*
33. *BTEC ND:* DDM.

B140 BSc Neuroscience
Duration: 3FT/4SW Hon
Entry Requirements: *GCE:* ABB. *SQAH:* AABBB. *SQAAH:* AB. *IB:*
33. *BTEC ND:* DDM.

BC15 BSc Pathology and Microbiology
Duration: 3FT/4SW Hon
Entry Requirements: *GCE:* ABB. *SQAH:* AABBB. *SQAAH:* AB. *IB:*
33. *BTEC ND:* DDM.

B120 BSc Physiological Science
Duration: 3FT Hon
Entry Requirements: *GCE:* ABB. *SQAH:* AABBB. *SQAAH:* AB. *IB:*
33. *BTEC ND:* DDM.

B80 UNIVERSITY OF THE WEST OF ENGLAND, BRISTOL
FRENCHAY CAMPUS
COLDHARBOUR LANE
BRISTOL BS16 1QY
t: +44 (0)117 32 83333 f: +44 (0)117 32 82810
e: admissions@uwe.ac.uk
// www.uwe.ac.uk

B160 BSc Physiotherapy
Duration: 3FT Hon CRB Check: Required
Entry Requirements: Interview required.

B84 BRUNEL UNIVERSITY
UXBRIDGE
MIDDLESEX UB8 3PH
t: 01895 265265 f: 01895 269790
e: admissions@brunel.ac.uk
// www.brunel.ac.uk

B160 BSc Physiotherapy
Duration: 3FT Hon CRB Check: Required
Entry Requirements: *GCE:* ABB. *SQAAH:* ABB. *IB:* 33. *BTEC NC:* DD. *BTEC ND:* DDD.

C15 CARDIFF UNIVERSITY
PO BOX 927
30-36 NEWPORT ROAD
CARDIFF CF24 0DE
t: 029 2087 9999 f: 029 2087 6138
e: admissions@cardiff.ac.uk
// www.cardiff.ac.uk

B111 BSc Biomedical Sciences (Anatomy)
Duration: 3FT Hon
Entry Requirements: *GCE:* AAB-ABB. *SQAH:* AAABB-AABBB. *SQAAH:* AAB-ABB. *IB:* 34. *BTEC ND:* DDD.

B112 BSc Biomedical Sciences (Anatomy)
Duration: 4SW Hon
Entry Requirements: *GCE:* AAB-ABB. *SQAH:* AAABB-AABBB. *SQAAH:* AAB-ABB. *IB:* 34. *BTEC ND:* DDD.

B142 BSc Biomedical Sciences (Neuroscience)
Duration: 3FT Hon
Entry Requirements: *GCE:* AAB-ABB. *SQAH:* AAABB-AABBB. *SQAAH:* AAB-ABB. *IB:* 34. *BTEC ND:* DDD.

B143 BSc Biomedical Sciences (Neuroscience)
Duration: 4SW Hon
Entry Requirements: *GCE:* AAB-ABB. *SQAH:* AAABB-AABBB. *SQAAH:* AAB-ABB. *IB:* 34. *BTEC ND:* DDD.

B121 BSc Biomedical Sciences (Physiology)
Duration: 3FT Hon
Entry Requirements: *GCE:* AAB-ABB. *SQAH:* AAABB-AABBB. *SQAAH:* AAB-ABB. *IB:* 34. *BTEC ND:* DDD.

B122 BSc Biomedical Sciences (Physiology)
Duration: 4SW Hon
Entry Requirements: *GCE:* AAB-ABB. *SQAH:* AAABB-AABBB. *SQAAH:* AAB-ABB. *IB:* 34. *BTEC ND:* DDD.

B160 BSc Physiotherapy
Duration: 3FT Hon CRB Check: Required
Entry Requirements: *GCE:* AAB. *SQAAH:* ABB. *IB:* 28. *BTEC NC:* DD. Interview required.

C20 UNIVERSITY OF WALES INSTITUTE, CARDIFF (UWIC)
ADMISSIONS UNIT
LLANDAFF CAMPUS
WESTERN AVENUE
CARDIFF CF5 2YB
t: 029 2041 6070 f: 029 2041 6286
e: admissions@uwic.ac.uk
// www.uwic.ac.uk

B985 BSc Podiatry
Duration: 3FT Hon CRB Check: Required
Entry Requirements: *GCE:* 280. *IB:* 25. *BTEC ND:* DMM. *OCR NED:* M2

C30 UNIVERSITY OF CENTRAL LANCASHIRE
PRESTON
LANCS PR1 2HE
t: 01772 201201 f: 01772 894954
e: uadmissions@uclan.ac.uk
// www.uclan.ac.uk

B140 BSc Neuroscience
Duration: 3FT Hon
Entry Requirements: *GCE:* 260-300. *SQAH:* BBBCC-BCCCC. *IB:* 28. *BTEC NC:* DD. *BTEC ND:* DMM. *OCR ND:* D

BB12 BSc Physiology and Pharmacology
Duration: 3FT Hon
Entry Requirements: *GCE:* 240-260. *SQAH:* BBBB-BBBC. *SQAAH:* AAA. *IB:* 28. *BTEC ND:* MMM. *OCR ND:* D *OCR NED:* M3

B160 BSc Physiotherapy
Duration: 3FT Hon CRB Check: Required
Entry Requirements: *GCE:* ABB. *IB:* 32. *BTEC NC:* DD. *BTEC ND:* DDM. *OCR ND:* D *OCR NED:* D2 Interview required.

CB61 BSc Sport & Exercise Physiology (Top-up)
Duration: 1FT Hon
Entry Requirements: HND required.

CB6C FdSc Sports Massage Practice
Duration: 2FT Fdg   CRB Check: Required
Entry Requirements: *GCE:* 160. *BTEC NC:* MM. *BTEC ND:* MPP.
OCR ND: M2 *OCR NED:* P2

C85 COVENTRY UNIVERSITY
THE STUDENT CENTRE
COVENTRY UNIVERSITY
1 GULSON RD
COVENTRY CV1 2JH
t: 024 7615 2222 f: 024 7615 2223
e: studentenquiries@coventry.ac.uk
// www.coventry.ac.uk

B160 BSc Physiotherapy
Duration: 3FT Hon   CRB Check: Required
Entry Requirements: *GCE:* BBB. *SQAH:* BBBBB. *IB:* 31. *BTEC ND:*
DDD. *OCR NED:* D1 Interview required.

C99 UNIVERSITY OF CUMBRIA
FUSEHILL STREET
CARLISLE
CUMBRIA CA1 2HH
t: 01228 616234 f: 01228 616235
// www.cumbria.ac.uk

B160 BSc Physiotherapy
Duration: 3FT Hon   CRB Check: Required
Entry Requirements: *Foundation:* Pass. *GCE:* 300. *IB:* 32. *BTEC
NC:* MM. *BTEC ND:* DDD. Interview required.

D65 UNIVERSITY OF DUNDEE
NETHERGATE
DUNDEE DD1 4HN
t: 01382 383838 f: 01382 388150
e: contactus@dundee.ac.uk
// www.dundee.ac.uk/admissions/
undergraduate/

B110 BSc Anatomical Sciences
Duration: 4FT Hon
Entry Requirements: *GCE:* BBB. *SQAH:* ABBB. *IB:* 30. *BTEC ND:*
DDM. Interview required.

B120 BSc Anatomical and Physiological Sciences
Duration: 4FT Hon
Entry Requirements: *GCE:* BBB. *SQAH:* ABBB. *IB:* 30. *BTEC ND:*
DDM.

B140 BSc Neuroscience
Duration: 4FT Hon
Entry Requirements: *GCE:* BBB. *SQAH:* ABBB. *IB:* 30. *BTEC ND:*
DDM.

B100 BSc Physiological Sciences
Duration: 4FT Hon
Entry Requirements: *GCE:* BBB. *SQAH:* ABBB. *IB:* 30. *BTEC ND:*
DDM.

D86 DURHAM UNIVERSITY
DURHAM UNIVERSITY
UNIVERSITY OFFICE
DURHAM DH1 3HP
t: 0191 334 2000 f: 0191 334 6055
e: admissions@durham.ac.uk
// www.durham.ac.uk

B190 BA Human Sciences with Foundation
Duration: 4FT Hon
Entry Requirements: Interview required.

E14 UNIVERSITY OF EAST ANGLIA
NORWICH NR4 7TJ
t: 01603 591515 f: 01603 458596
e: admissions@uea.ac.uk
// www.uea.ac.uk

B160 BSc Physiotherapy
Duration: 3FT Hon   CRB Check: Required
Entry Requirements: *GCE:* 300. *SQAH:* AABBB. *SQAAH:* ABB. *IB:*
32. *BTEC NC:* DM. *BTEC ND:* DDM. Interview required.

E28 UNIVERSITY OF EAST LONDON
DOCKLANDS CAMPUS
UNIVERSITY WAY
LONDON E16 2RD
t: 020 8223 3333 f: 020 8223 2978
e: study@uel.ac.uk
// www.uel.ac.uk

X3B1 BA Early Childhood Studies with Human Biology
Duration: 3FT Hon
Entry Requirements: *GCE:* 200. *IB:* 24. *BTEC NC:* DM. *BTEC ND:*
MMP. *OCR ND:* M1 *OCR NED:* P1

B1L6 BA/BSc Human Biology/Anthropology
Duration: 3FT Hon
Entry Requirements: *GCE:* 200. *IB:* 24. *BTEC NC:* DM. *BTEC ND:*
MMP. *OCR ND:* M1 *OCR NED:* P1

B1P3 BA/BSc Human Biology/Media Studies
Duration: 3FT Hon
Entry Requirements: *GCE:* 200. *IB:* 24. *BTEC NC:* DM. *BTEC ND:*
MMP. *OCR ND:* M1 *OCR NED:* P1

B9BC BSc Clinical Science with Medical Physiology
Duration: 3FT Hon
Entry Requirements: *GCE:* 200. *IB:* 24. *BTEC NC:* DM. *BTEC ND:*
MMP. *OCR ND:* M1 *OCR NED:* P1

F4B1 BSc Forensic Science with Human Biology
Duration: 3FT Hon
Entry Requirements: *GCE:* 240. *IB:* 24. *BTEC NC:* DD. *BTEC ND:* MMM. *OCR ND:* M1 *OCR NED:* P1

B9B1 BSc Health Promotion with Human Biology
Duration: 3FT Hon
Entry Requirements: *GCE:* 200. *IB:* 24. *BTEC NC:* DM. *BTEC ND:* MMP. *OCR ND:* M1 *OCR NED:* P1

B1BX BSc Human Biology with Clinical Science
Duration: 3FT Hon
Entry Requirements: *GCE:* 200. *IB:* 24. *BTEC NC:* DM. *BTEC ND:* MMP. *OCR ND:* M1 *OCR NED:* P1

B1X3 BSc Human Biology with Early Childhood Studies
Duration: 3FT Hon
Entry Requirements: *GCE:* 200. *IB:* 24. *BTEC NC:* DM. *BTEC ND:* MMP. *OCR ND:* M1 *OCR NED:* P1

B1BF BSc Human Biology with Pharmacology
Duration: 3FT Hon
Entry Requirements: Contact the institution for details.

B1B9 BSc Human Biology with Public Health
Duration: 3FT Hon
Entry Requirements: *GCE:* 200. *IB:* 24. *BTEC NC:* DM. *BTEC ND:* MMP. *OCR ND:* M1 *OCR NED:* P1

B1L3 BSc Human Biology with Sociology (Professional Development)
Duration: 3FT Hon
Entry Requirements: *GCE:* 200. *IB:* 24. *BTEC NC:* DM. *BTEC ND:* MMP. *OCR ND:* M1 *OCR NED:* P1

B1X1 BSc Human Biology with Special Needs and Inclusive Education
Duration: 3FT Hon
Entry Requirements: *GCE:* 200. *IB:* 24. *BTEC NC:* DM. *BTEC ND:* MMP. *OCR ND:* M1 *OCR NED:* P1

B1C6 BSc Human Biology with Sports Coaching
Duration: 3FT Hon
Entry Requirements: *GCE:* 200. *IB:* 24. *BTEC NC:* DM. *BTEC ND:* MMP. *OCR ND:* M1 *OCR NED:* P1

B1B2 BSc Human Biology with Toxicology
Duration: 3FT Hon
Entry Requirements: *GCE:* 200. *IB:* 24. *BTEC NC:* DM. *BTEC ND:* MMP. *OCR ND:* M1 *OCR NED:* P1

J7B1 BSc Medical Biotechnology with Human Biology
Duration: 3FT Hon
Entry Requirements: Contact the institution for details.

C5B1 BSc Medical Microbiology with Human Biology
Duration: 3FT Hon
Entry Requirements: *GCE:* 200. *IB:* 24. *BTEC NC:* DM. *BTEC ND:* MMP. *OCR ND:* M1 *OCR NED:* P1

B121 BSc Medical Physiology
Duration: 3FT Hon
Entry Requirements: *GCE:* 200. *IB:* 24.

B1C7 BSc Medical Physiology with Biochemistry
Duration: 3FT Hon
Entry Requirements: Contact the institution for details.

B191 BSc Medical Physiology with Clinical Science
Duration: 3FT Hon
Entry Requirements: Contact the institution for details.

B190 BSc Medical Physiology with Human Biology
Duration: 3FT Hon
Entry Requirements: Contact the institution for details.

B1C5 BSc Medical Physiology with Immunology
Duration: 3FT Hon
Entry Requirements: Contact the institution for details.

B2B1 BSc Pharmacology with Human Biology
Duration: 3FT Hon
Entry Requirements: *GCE:* 200. *IB:* 24. *BTEC NC:* DM. *BTEC ND:* MMP. *OCR ND:* M1 *OCR NED:* P1

B160 BSc Physiotherapy
Duration: 3FT Hon
Entry Requirements: *GCE:* 280. *IB:* 28.

B330 BSc Podiatric Medicine
Duration: 3FT Hon
Entry Requirements: *GCE:* 240. *IB:* 26.

C6BC BSc Sports & Exercise Science with Human Biology
Duration: 3FT Hon
Entry Requirements: *GCE:* 200. *IB:* 24. *BTEC NC:* DM. *BTEC ND:* MMP.

C6B1 BSc Sports Development with Human Biology
Duration: 3FT Hon
Entry Requirements: *GCE:* 200. *IB:* 24. *BTEC NC:* DM. *BTEC ND:* MMP. *OCR ND:* M1 *OCR NED:* P1

B2BC BSc Toxicology with Human Biology
Duration: 3FT Hon
Entry Requirements: *GCE:* 200. *IB:* 24. *BTEC NC:* DM. *BTEC ND:* MMP. *OCR ND:* M1 *OCR NED:* P1

BB21 BSc Toxicology/Human Biology
Duration: 3FT Hon
Entry Requirements: *GCE:* 200. *IB:* 24. *BTEC NC:* DM. *BTEC ND:* MMP. *OCR ND:* M1 *OCR NED:* P1

BN12 BSc/BA Human Biology/Business Management
Duration: 3FT Hon
Entry Requirements: Contact the institution for details.

E56 THE UNIVERSITY OF EDINBURGH
STUDENT RECRUITMENT & ADMISSIONS
57 GEORGE SQUARE
EDINBURGH EH8 9JU
t: 0131 650 4360 f: 0131 651 1236
e: sra.enquiries@ed.ac.uk
// www.ed.ac.uk/studying/undergraduate/

B100 BSc Medical Sciences
Duration: 4FT Hon
Entry Requirements: *GCE:* BBB. *SQAH:* AABB-BBBB.

B140 BSc Neuroscience
Duration: 4FT Hon
Entry Requirements: *GCE:* AAA-ABB. *SQAH:* AAAA-ABBB.

B120 BSc Physiology
Duration: 4FT Hon
Entry Requirements: *GCE:* AAA-ABB. *SQAH:* AAAA-ABBB.

E59 EDINBURGH NAPIER UNIVERSITY
CRAIGLOCKHART CAMPUS
EDINBURGH EH14 1DJ
t: +44 (0)8452 60 60 40 f: 0131 455 6464
e: info@napier.ac.uk
// www.napier.ac.uk

CB61 BSc Sport and Exercise Science (Exercise Physiology)
Duration: 3FT/4FT Ord/Hon
Entry Requirements: *GCE:* 260.

G28 UNIVERSITY OF GLASGOW
THE UNIVERSITY OF GLASGOW
THE FRASER BUILDING
65 HILLHEAD STREET
GLASGOW G12 8QF
t: 0141 330 6062 f: 0141 330 2961
e: student.recruitment@glasgow.ac.uk
// www.glasgow.ac.uk

B110 BSc Anatomy
Duration: 4FT Hon
Entry Requirements: *GCE:* ABB. *SQAH:* AAAB-BBBB. *IB:* 32. *BTEC ND:* DDM.

B111 BSc Anatomy (Faster Route)
Duration: 3FT Hon
Entry Requirements: *GCE:* AAA. *SQAAH:* AAA. *IB:* 38.

GB41 BSc Computing Science/Physiology (Neuroinformatics)
Duration: 4FT Hon
Entry Requirements: *GCE:* ABB. *SQAH:* AAAB-BBBB. *IB:* 32.

B150 BSc Human Biology
Duration: 3FT Ord
Entry Requirements: *GCE:* ABB *SQAH:* AAAB-BBBB. *IB:* 32. *BTEC ND:* DDM.

B140 BSc Neuroscience
Duration: 4FT Hon
Entry Requirements: *GCE:* ABB. *SQAH:* AAAB-BBBB. *IB:* 32. *BTEC ND:* DDM.

B141 BSc Neuroscience (Faster Route)
Duration: 3FT Hon
Entry Requirements: *GCE:* AAA. *SQAAH:* AAA. *IB:* 38.

B120 BSc Physiology
Duration: 4FT Hon
Entry Requirements: *GCE:* ABB. *SQAH:* AAAB-BBBB. *IB:* 32. *BTEC ND:* DDM.

BC61 BSc Physiology & Sports Science (Faster Route)
Duration: 3FT Hon
Entry Requirements: *GCE:* AAA. *SQAAH:* AAA. *IB:* 38.

B121 BSc Physiology (Faster Route)
Duration: 3FT Hon
Entry Requirements: *GCE:* AAA. *SQAAH:* AAA. *IB:* 38.

BC16 BSc Physiology and Sports Science
Duration: 4FT Hon
Entry Requirements: *GCE:* ABB. *SQAH:* AAAB-BBBB. *IB:* 32. *BTEC ND:* DDM.

BC46 BSc Physiology, Sports Science and Nutrition
Duration: 4FT Hon
Entry Requirements: *GCE:* ABB. *SQAH:* AAAB-BBBB. *IB:* 32. *BTEC ND:* DDM.

BC64 BSc Physiology, Sports Science and Nutrition (Faster Route)
Duration: 3FT Hon
Entry Requirements: *GCE:* AAA. *SQAAH:* AAA. *IB:* 38.

BC18 BSc Physiology/Psychology
Duration: 4FT Hon
Entry Requirements: *GCE:* AAA. *SQAH:* AAAA-AABB. *IB:* 32. *BTEC ND:* DDD.

G42 GLASGOW CALEDONIAN UNIVERSITY
STUDENT RECRUITMENT & ADMISSIONS SERVICE
CITY CAMPUS
COWCADDENS ROAD
GLASGOW G4 0BA
t: 0141 331 3000 f: 0141 331 8676
e: undergraduate@gcu.ac.uk
// www.gcu.ac.uk

B120 BSc Human Biosciences
Duration: 4FT Hon
Entry Requirements: *GCE:* BCC. *SQAH:* AAA-BBBC. *IB:* 24.

B160 BSc Physiotherapy
Duration: 4FT Hon CRB Check: Required
Entry Requirements: *GCE:* BBB. *SQAH:* BBBBBC-BBBBC. *IB:* 32. *BTEC ND:* DDM. *OCR NED:* M1

B985 BSc Podiatry
Duration: 4FT Hon CRB Check: Required
Entry Requirements: *GCE:* CCD. *SQAH:* BBCC. *IB:* 26.

H36 UNIVERSITY OF HERTFORDSHIRE
UNIVERSITY ADMISSIONS SERVICE
COLLEGE LANE
HATFIELD
HERTS AL10 9AB
t: 01707 284800
// www.herts.ac.uk

G4B1 BSc Computing/Human Biology
Duration: 3FT/4SW Hon
Entry Requirements: Contact the institution for details.

L1B1 BSc Economics/Human Biology
Duration: 3FT/4SW Hon
Entry Requirements: Contact the institution for details.

Q1B1 BSc English Language & Communication/Human Biology
Duration: 3FT/4SW Hon
Entry Requirements: Contact the institution for details.

F9B1 BSc Environmental Studies/Human Biology
Duration: 3FT/4SW Hon
Entry Requirements: Contact the institution for details.

RB81 BSc European Studies/Human Biology
Duration: 3FT/4SW Hon
Entry Requirements: Contact the institution for details.

G9B1 BSc Financial Mathematics/Human Biology
Duration: 3FT/4SW Hon
Entry Requirements: *GCE:* 220.

B1G4 BSc Human Biology/Computing
Duration: 3FT/4SW Hon
Entry Requirements: *IB:* 25.

B1L1 BSc Human Biology/Economics
Duration: 3FT/4SW Hon
Entry Requirements: *IB:* 25.

B1Q1 BSc Human Biology/English Language & Communication
Duration: 3FT/4SW Hon
Entry Requirements: Contact the institution for details.

B1F9 BSc Human Biology/Environmental Studies
Duration: 3FT/4SW Hon
Entry Requirements: *IB:* 25.

B1R8 BSc Human Biology/European Studies
Duration: 3FT/4SW Hon
Entry Requirements: *IB:* 25.

B1G9 BSc Human Biology/Financial Mathematics
Duration: 3FT/4SW Hon
Entry Requirements: *GCE:* 220.

B1R1 BSc Human Biology/French
Duration: 3FT/4SW Hon
Entry Requirements: *IB:* 25.

B1P5 BSc Human Biology/Journalism & Media Cultures
Duration: 3FT/4SW Hon
Entry Requirements: Contact the institution for details.

B1M1 BSc Human Biology/Law
Duration: 3FT/4SW Hon
Entry Requirements: Contact the institution for details.

B1G1 BSc Human Biology/Mathematics
Duration: 3FT/4SW Hon
Entry Requirements: Contact the institution for details.

B1C8 BSc Human Biology/Psychology
Duration: 3FT/4SW Hon
Entry Requirements: Contact the institution for details.

B1R4 BSc Human Biology/Spanish
Duration: 3FT/4SW Hon
Entry Requirements: Contact the institution for details.

B1C6 BSc Human Biology/Sports Studies
Duration: 3FT/4SW Hon
Entry Requirements: *IB:* 25.

B1N8 BSc Human Biology/Tourism
Duration: 3FT/4SW Hon
Entry Requirements: *IB:* 25.

P5B1 BSc Journalism & Media Cultures/Human Biology
Duration: 3FT/4SW Hon
Entry Requirements: Contact the institution for details.

M1B1 BSc Law/Human Biology
Duration: 3FT/4SW Hon
Entry Requirements: Contact the institution for details.

G1B1 BSc Mathematics/Human Biology
Duration: 3FT/4SW Hon
Entry Requirements: Contact the institution for details.

C1B1 BSc Physiology
Duration: 3FT/4SW Hon
Entry Requirements: *GCE:* 240.

B101 BSc Physiology with a year in Europe
Duration: 4FT Hon
Entry Requirements: *GCE:* 240.

B102 BSc Physiology with a year in North America
Duration: 4FT Hon
Entry Requirements: *GCE:* 240.

B160 BSc Physiotherapy
Duration: 3FT Hon   CRB Check: Required
Entry Requirements: *GCE:* 300. Interview required.

C8B1 BSc Psychology/Human Biology
Duration: 3FT/4SW Hon
Entry Requirements: Contact the institution for details.

C6B1 BSc Sports Studies/Human Biology
Duration: 3FT/4SW Hon
Entry Requirements: Contact the institution for details.

N8B1 BSc Tourism/Human Biology
Duration: 3FT/4SW Hon
Entry Requirements: Contact the institution for details.

H60 THE UNIVERSITY OF HUDDERSFIELD
QUEENSGATE
HUDDERSFIELD HD1 3DH
t: 01484 473969 f: 01484 472765
e: admissionsandrecords@hud.ac.uk
// www.hud.ac.uk

B150 BSc Human Biology
Duration: 3FT Hon
Entry Requirements: *GCE:* 280. *SQAH:* BBB. *IB:* 26.

B160 BSc Physiotherapy
Duration: 3FT Hon   CRB Check: Required
Entry Requirements: *GCE:* 300. *SQAH:* BBBB. *IB:* 30. *BTEC ND:* DMM. Interview required.

B985 BSc Podiatry
Duration: 3FT Hon   CRB Check: Required
Entry Requirements: *GCE:* 300. *SQAH:* BBBC. *IB:* 26. *BTEC ND:* DMM. Interview required.

K12 KEELE UNIVERSITY
STAFFS ST5 5BG
t: 01782 734005 f: 01782 632343
e: undergraduate@keele.ac.uk
// www.keele.ac.uk

NB41 BSc Accounting and Neuroscience
Duration: 3FT Hon
Entry Requirements: *GCE:* 280-300.

BT17 BSc American Studies and Neuroscience
Duration: 3FT Hon
Entry Requirements: *GCE:* 280-300.

FB71 BSc Applied Environmental Science and Neuroscience
Duration: 3FT Hon
Entry Requirements: *GCE:* 300.

CB81 BSc Applied Psychology and Neuroscience
Duration: 4FT Deg
Entry Requirements: *GCE:* 280-300.

BF15 BSc Astrophysics and Neuroscience
Duration: 3FT Hon
Entry Requirements: *GCE:* 300-320.

BC17 BSc Biochemistry and Neuroscience
Duration: 3FT Hon
Entry Requirements: *GCE:* 300.

BF11 BSc Chemistry and Neuroscience
Duration: 3FT Hon
Entry Requirements: *GCE:* 300.

BG14 BSc Computer Science and Neuroscience
Duration: 3FT Hon
Entry Requirements: *GCE:* 280-300.

GB41 BSc Creative Computing and Neurosciences
Duration: 3FT Hon
Entry Requirements: *GCE:* 280-300.

BM19 BSc Criminology and Neuroscience
Duration: 3FT Hon
Entry Requirements: *GCE:* 280-300.

BL11 BSc Economics and Neuroscience
Duration: 3FT Hon
Entry Requirements: *GCE:* 280-300.

BX13 BSc Educational Studies and Neuroscience
Duration: 3FT Hon
Entry Requirements: *GCE:* 280-300.

BQ13 BSc English and Neuroscience
Duration: 3FT Hon
Entry Requirements: *GCE:* 300-320.

PB3C BSc Film Studies and Human Biology
Duration: 3FT Hon
Entry Requirements: *GCE:* 300.

PB3D BSc Film Studies and Neuroscience
Duration: 3FT Hon
Entry Requirements: *GCE:* 300.

BN13 BSc Finance and Neuroscience
Duration: 3FT Hon
Entry Requirements: *GCE:* 280-300.

FB41 BSc Forensic Science and Neuroscience
Duration: 3FT Hon
Entry Requirements: *GCE:* 300.

BF18 BSc Geography and Neuroscience
Duration: 3FT Hon
Entry Requirements: *GCE:* 300.

BF16 BSc Geology and Neuroscience
Duration: 3FT Hon
Entry Requirements: *GCE:* 300.

BL17 BSc Human Geography and Neuroscience
Duration: 3FT Hon
Entry Requirements: *GCE:* 300.

BN16 BSc Human Resource Management and Neuroscience
Duration: 3FT Hon
Entry Requirements: *GCE:* 280-300.

BG15 BSc Information Systems and Neuroscience
Duration: 3FT Hon
Entry Requirements: *GCE:* 280-300.

BLC2 BSc International Relations and Neuroscience
Duration: 3FT Hon
Entry Requirements: *GCE:* 280-300.

BM11 BSc Law and Neuroscience
Duration: 3FT Hon
Entry Requirements: *GCE:* 280-300.

BG11 BSc Mathematics and Neuroscience
Duration: 3FT Hon
Entry Requirements: *GCE:* 280-300.

PB31 BSc Media, Communications & Culture and Neuroscience
Duration: 3FT Hon
Entry Requirements: *GCE:* 280-300.

BFC1 BSc Medicinal Chemistry and Neuroscience
Duration: 3FT Hon
Entry Requirements: *GCE:* 300.

BW13 BSc Music Technology and Neuroscience
Duration: 3FT Hon
Entry Requirements: *GCE:* 280-300.

BFC8 BSc Neuroscience and Physical Geography
Duration: 3FT Hon
Entry Requirements: *GCE:* 300.

BF13 BSc Neuroscience and Physics
Duration: 3FT Hon
Entry Requirements: *GCE:* 300-320.

BL12 BSc Neuroscience and Politics
Duration: 3FT Hon
Entry Requirements: *GCE:* 280-300.

BC18 BSc Neuroscience and Psychology
Duration: 3FT Hon
Entry Requirements: *GCE:* 280-300.

B143 BSc Neuroscience with Science Foundation Year
Duration: 4FT Hon
Entry Requirements: *GCE:* 160.

B160 BSc Physiotherapy
Duration: 3FT Hon   CRB Check: Required
Entry Requirements: *GCE:* ABB. *SQAAH:* BBB. *IB:* 28. *BTEC ND:* DDD. Interview required.

B1B9 BSc Physiotherapy with Health Foundation Year
Duration: 4FT Hon   CRB Check: Required
Entry Requirements: *GCE:* BBB. *SQAAH:* BBB. *IB:* 28. *BTEC ND:* DDM. Interview required.

GB71 BSc Smart Systems and Neuroscience
Duration: 3FT Hon
Entry Requirements: *GCE:* 280-300.

K60 KING'S COLLEGE LONDON (UNIVERSITY OF LONDON)
STRAND
LONDON WC2R 2LS
t: 020 7848 7070 f: 020 7848 7171
e: prospective@kcl.ac.uk
// www.kcl.ac.uk

B150 BSc Human Sciences
Duration: 3FT Hon
Entry Requirements: *GCE:* AABc. *SQAH:* AAABB. *IB:* 36.

B140 BSc Neuroscience
Duration: 3FT Hon
Entry Requirements: *GCE:* AABc. *SQAH:* AAABB. *IB:* 36.

B120 BSc Physiology
Duration: 3FT Hon
Entry Requirements: *GCE:* AABc. *SQAH:* AAABB. *IB:* 36.

B160 BSc Physiotherapy
Duration: 3FT Hon   CRB Check: Required
Entry Requirements: *GCE:* ABBc. *SQAH:* AABBB. *IB:* 34.

K84 KINGSTON UNIVERSITY
STUDENT INFORMATION & ADVICE CENTRE
COOPER HOUSE
40-46 SURBITON ROAD
KINGSTON UPON THAMES KT1 2HX
t: 0844 8552177 f: 020 8547 7080
e: aps@kingston.ac.uk
// www.kingston.ac.uk

B100 BSc Human Biology
Duration: 3FT Hon
Entry Requirements: *GCE:* 180-280.

B101 BSc Human Biology
Duration: 4SW Hon
Entry Requirements: *GCE:* 180-280.

B102 BSc Human Biology (including year 0)
Duration: 4FT Hon
Entry Requirements: *GCE:* 60.

BB14 BSc Human Biology and Nutrition
Duration: 3FT Hon
Entry Requirements: *GCE:* 200-280.

L23 UNIVERSITY OF LEEDS
THE UNIVERSITY OF LEEDS
WOODHOUSE LANE
LEEDS LS2 9JT
t: 0113 343 3999
e: admissions@leeds.ac.uk
// www.leeds.ac.uk

B101 BSc Clinical Physiology (Cardiology)
Duration: 4FT Hon   CRB Check: Required
Entry Requirements: *GCE:* ABB. *SQAAH:* CCC. *BTEC ND:* DDD.

B120 BSc Human Physiology
Duration: 3FT/4FT Hon
Entry Requirements: *GCE:* AAA-ABB. *SQAH:* AAAAA-AAABB. *SQAAH:* AAA-ABB. *BTEC ND:* DDD.

B100 BSc Medical Sciences
Duration: 3FT/4FT Hon
Entry Requirements: *GCE:* AAA-ABB. *SQAH:* AAAAA-AAABB. *SQAAH:* AAA-ABB. *BTEC ND:* DDD.

B140 BSc Neuroscience
Duration: 3FT/4FT Hon
Entry Requirements: *GCE:* AAA-BBB. *SQAH:* AAAAA-AABBB. *SQAAH:* AAA-BBB. *BTEC ND:* DDD.

BC16 BSc Sports Science & Physiology
Duration: 3FT/4FT Hon
Entry Requirements: *GCE:* AAB-BBB. *SQAAH:* AAB-BBB. *BTEC NC:* DD. *BTEC ND:* DDD.

L27 LEEDS METROPOLITAN UNIVERSITY
COURSE ENQUIRIES OFFICE
CITY SITE
LEEDS LS1 3HE
t: 0113 81 23113 f: 0113 81 23129
// www.leedsmet.ac.uk

BB12 BSc Biomedical Sciences (Physiology/Pharmacology)
Duration: 3FT Hon
Entry Requirements: *GCE:* 160. *IB:* 24.

B160 BSc Physiotherapy
Duration: 3FT Hon   CRB Check: Required
Entry Requirements: *GCE:* 280. *IB:* 30.

L34 UNIVERSITY OF LEICESTER
UNIVERSITY ROAD
LEICESTER LE1 7RH
t: 0116 252 5281 f: 0116 252 2447
e: admissions@le.ac.uk
// www.le.ac.uk

B1B2 BSc Biological Sciences (Physiology with Pharmacology)
Duration: 3FT Hon
Entry Requirements: *GCE:* ABB. *SQAH:* AABBB. *SQAAH:* ABB. *IB:* 32. *BTEC ND:* DDM.

B120 BSc Medical Physiology
Duration: 3FT Hon
Entry Requirements: *GCE:* ABB. *SQAH:* AABBB. *SQAAH:* ABB. *IB:* 32. *BTEC ND:* DDM.

L41 THE UNIVERSITY OF LIVERPOOL
THE FOUNDATION BUILDING
BROWNLOW HILL
LIVERPOOL L69 7ZX
t: 0151 794 2000 f: 0151 708 6502
e: ugrecruitment@liv.ac.uk
// www.liv.ac.uk

B110 BSc Anatomy and Human Biology
Duration: 3FT Hon
Entry Requirements: *GCE:* AAB-ABB. *SQAAH:* AAB-ABB. *IB:* 33. Interview required.

V4B1 BSc Evolutionary Anthropology
Duration: 3FT Hon
Entry Requirements: *GCE:* ABB. *SQAH:* AABBB. *SQAAH:* ABB. *IB:* 33. *BTEC ND:* DDM.

B120 BSc Physiology
Duration: 3FT Hon
Entry Requirements: *GCE:* ABB-BBB. *SQAAH:* ABB-BBB. *IB:* 32. Interview required.

B160 BSc Physiotherapy
Duration: 3FT Hon   CRB Check: Required
Entry Requirements: *GCE:* ABB. *IB:* 30. *BTEC ND:* DDM.

L46 LIVERPOOL HOPE UNIVERSITY
HOPE PARK
LIVERPOOL L16 9JD
t: 0151 291 3295 f: 0151 291 3444
e: admission@hope.ac.uk
// www.hope.ac.uk

XB31 BA Education and Human Biology
Duration: 3FT Hon   CRB Check: Required
Entry Requirements: *GCE:* 260-320. *IB:* 25.

X1BC BA Primary Teaching with Human Biology
Duration: 4FT Hon   CRB Check: Required
Entry Requirements: *GCE:* 300. *IB:* 25. Interview required.

BG15 BSc Human Biology and Information Technology
Duration: 3FT Hon
Entry Requirements: *GCE:* 260-320. *IB:* 25.

BC18 BSc Human Biology and Psychology
Duration: 3FT Hon
Entry Requirements: *GCE:* 260-320. *IB:* 25.

CB61 BSc Human Biology and Sport Studies
Duration: 3FT Hon
Entry Requirements: *GCE:* 260-320. *IB:* 25.

L75 LONDON SOUTH BANK UNIVERSITY
103 BOROUGH ROAD
LONDON SE1 0AA
t: 020 7815 7815 f: 020 7815 8273
e: enquiry@lsbu.ac.uk
// www.lsbu.ac.uk

B150 BSc Bioscience (Human Biology)
Duration: 3FT/4SW Hon
Entry Requirements: *GCE:* 200. *IB:* 24.

L79 LOUGHBOROUGH UNIVERSITY
LOUGHBOROUGH
LEICESTERSHIRE LE11 3TU
t: 01509 223522 f: 01509 223905
e: admissions@lboro.ac.uk
// www.lboro.ac.uk

B150 BSc Human Biology
Duration: 3FT Hon
Entry Requirements: *GCE:* 300-320. *SQAAH:* BB. *BTEC ND:* DDM.

B151 BSc Human Biology
Duration: 4SW Hon
Entry Requirements: *GCE:* 300-320. *SQAAH:* BB. *BTEC ND:* DMM.

M20 THE UNIVERSITY OF MANCHESTER
OXFORD ROAD
MANCHESTER M13 9PL
t: 0161 275 2077 f: 0161 275 2106
e: ug-admissions@manchester.ac.uk
// www.manchester.ac.uk

B110 BSc Anatomical Sciences
Duration: 3FT Hon
Entry Requirements: *GCE:* AAA-ABB. *SQAH:* AAAAA-AAABB.
SQAAH: AAA-ABB. Interview required.

B111 BSc Anatomical Sciences with Industrial/Professional Experience (4 years)
Duration: 4SW Hon
Entry Requirements: *GCE:* AAA-ABB. *SQAH:* AAAAA-AAABB.
SQAAH: AAA-ABB. *BTEC ND:* DDM. Interview required.

B114 BSc Anatomical Sciences with a Modern Language (4 years)
Duration: 4FT Hon
Entry Requirements: *GCE:* AAA-ABB. *SQAH:* AAAAA-AAABB.
SQAAH: AAA-ABB. *BTEC ND:* DDM. Interview required.

BC18 BSc Cognitive Neuroscience and Psychology
Duration: 3FT Hon
Entry Requirements: *GCE:* AAA-ABB. *SQAH:* AAAAA-AAABB.
SQAAH: AAA-ABB. *BTEC ND:* DDM. Interview required.

BCC8 BSc Cognitive Neuroscience and Psychology with Industrial/Professional Experience
Duration: 4SW Hon   CRB Check: Required
Entry Requirements: *GCE:* AAA-ABB. *SQAH:* AAAAA-AAABB.
SQAAH: AAA-ABB. *BTEC ND:* DDD. Interview required.

B140 BSc Neuroscience
Duration: 3FT Hon
Entry Requirements: *GCE:* AAA-ABB. *SQAH:* AAAAA-AAABB.
SQAAH: AAA-ABB. *BTEC ND:* DDM. Interview required.

B143 BSc Neuroscience with Industrial/Professional Experience (4 years)
Duration: 4SW Hon
Entry Requirements: *GCE:* AAA-ABB. *SQAH:* AAAAA-AAABB.
SQAAH: AAA-ABB. *BTEC ND:* DDM. Interview required.

B144 BSc Neuroscience with a Modern Language (4 years)
Duration: 4FT Hon
Entry Requirements: *GCE:* AAA-ABB. *SQAH:* AAAAA-AAABB.
SQAAH: AAA-ABB. *BTEC ND:* DDM. Interview required.

BB12 BSc Pharmacology and Physiology
Duration: 3FT Hon
Entry Requirements: *GCE:* AAA-ABB. *SQAH:* AAAAA-AAABB.
SQAAH: AAA-ABB. *BTEC ND:* DDM. Interview required.

BBC2 BSc Pharmacology and Physiology with Industrial/Professional Experience (4 years)
Duration: 4SW Hon
Entry Requirements: *GCE:* AAA-ABB. *SQAH:* AAAAA-AAABB.
SQAAH: AAA-ABB. *BTEC ND:* DDM. Interview required.

B120 BSc Physiology
Duration: 3FT Hon
Entry Requirements: *GCE:* AAA-ABB. *SQAH:* AAAAA-AAABB.
SQAAH: AAA-ABB. *BTEC ND:* DDM. Interview required.

B121 BSc Physiology with Industrial/Professional Experience (4 years)
Duration: 4SW Hon
Entry Requirements: *GCE:* AAA-ABB. *SQAH:* AAAAA-AAABB.
SQAAH: AAA-ABB. *BTEC ND:* DDM. Interview required.

B122 BSc Physiology with a Modern Language (4 years)
Duration: 4FT Hon
Entry Requirements: *GCE:* AAA-ABB. *SQAH:* AAAAA-AAABB.
SQAAH: AAA-ABB. *BTEC ND:* DDM. Interview required.

B141 MNeurosc Neuroscience
Duration: 4FT Hon
Entry Requirements: *GCE:* AAA-ABB. *SQAH:* AAAAA-AAABB.
SQAAH: AAA-ABB. *BTEC ND:* DDM. Interview required.

M40 THE MANCHESTER METROPOLITAN UNIVERSITY
ADMISSIONS OFFICE
ALL SAINTS (GMS)
ALL SAINTS
MANCHESTER M15 6BH
t: 0161 247 2000
// www.mmu.ac.uk

B120 BSc Clinical Physiology
Duration: 4FT Hon
Entry Requirements: *GCE:* 240-280. *IB:* 27. *BTEC ND:* DMM.
Interview required.

B121 BSc Physiology (Physical Activity and Health)
Duration: 3FT/4SW Hon
Entry Requirements: *GCE:* 240-280. *IB:* 27.

B122 BSc Physiology (Physical Activity and Health) (Foundation)
Duration: 4FT/5SW Hon
Entry Requirements: *GCE:* 80. *IB:* 24.

www.ucas.com

at the heart of connecting people to higher education

B160 BSc Physiotherapy
Duration: 3FT Hon   CRB Check: Required
Entry Requirements: *GCE:* ABB. *SQAH:* AABBB. *SQAAH:* B. *IB:* 30.
BTEC ND: DDM. Interview required.

N21 NEWCASTLE UNIVERSITY
KING'S GATE
NEWCASTLE UPON TYNE NE1 7RU
t: 0191 208 3333 f: 0191 222 6143
// www.ncl.ac.uk

B100 BSc Physiological Sciences
Duration: 3FT Hon
Entry Requirements: *GCE:* AAB-BBB. *SQAH:* AAAB. *IB:* 32.

N28 NEW COLLEGE DURHAM
FRAMWELLGATE MOOR CENTRE
DURHAM DH1 5ES
t: 0191 375 4210/4211 f: 0191 375 4222
e: admissions@newdur.ac.uk
// www.newdur.ac.uk

B985 BSc Podiatry (with state registration)
Duration: 3FT Hon
Entry Requirements: *GCE:* 160. Interview required.

N38 UNIVERSITY OF NORTHAMPTON
PARK CAMPUS
BOUGHTON GREEN ROAD
NORTHAMPTON NN2 7AL
t: 0800 358 2232 f: 01604 722083
e: admissions@northampton.ac.uk
// www.northampton.ac.uk

N5BD BA Advertising/Human Bioscience
Duration: 3FT Hon
Entry Requirements: *GCE:* 260-280. *SQAH:* AAA-BBBB. *IB:* 24.
BTEC NC: DD. *BTEC ND:* DMM. *OCR ND:* D *OCR NED:* M2

N1B1 BA Business/Human Bioscience
Duration: 3FT Hon
Entry Requirements: *GCE:* 260-280. *SQAH:* AAA-BBBB. *IB:* 24.
BTEC NC: DD. *BTEC ND:* DMM. *OCR ND:* D *OCR NED:* M2

W8B1 BA Creative Writing/Human Bioscience
Duration: 3FT Hon
Entry Requirements: *GCE:* 260-280. *SQAH:* AAA-BBBB. *IB:* 24.
BTEC NC: DD. *BTEC ND:* DMM. *OCR ND:* D *OCR NED:* M2

W4B1 BA Drama/Human Bioscience
Duration: 3FT Hon
Entry Requirements: *GCE:* 260-280. *SQAH:* AAA-BBBB. *IB:* 24.
BTEC NC: DD. *BTEC ND:* DMM. *OCR ND:* D *OCR NED:* M2
Interview required.

L1B1 BA Economics/Human Bioscience
Duration: 3FT Hon
Entry Requirements: *GCE:* 260-280. *SQAH:* AAA-BBBB. *IB:* 24.
BTEC NC: DD. *BTEC ND:* DMM. *OCR ND:* D *OCR NED:* M2

X3B1 BA Education Studies/Human Bioscience
Duration: 3FT Hon
Entry Requirements: *GCE:* 260-280. *SQAH:* AAA-BBBB. *IB:* 24.
BTEC NC: DD. *BTEC ND:* DMM. *OCR ND:* D *OCR NED:* M2

Q3B1 BA English/Human Bioscience
Duration: 3FT Hon
Entry Requirements: *GCE:* 260-280. *SQAH:* AAA-BBBB. *IB:* 24.
BTEC NC: DD. *BTEC ND:* DMM. *OCR ND:* D *OCR NED:* M2

N8BD BA Events Management/Human Bioscience
Duration: 3FT Hon
Entry Requirements: *GCE:* 260-280. *SQAH:* AAA-BBBB. *IB:* 24.
BTEC NC: DD. *BTEC ND:* DMM. *OCR ND:* D *OCR NED:* M2

W6B1 BA Film & Television Studies/Human Bioscience
Duration: 3FT Hon
Entry Requirements: *GCE:* 260 280. *SQAH:* AAA-BBBB. *IB:* 24.
BTEC NC: DD. *BTEC ND:* DMM. *OCR ND:* D *OCR NED:* M2

L4B1 BA Health Studies/Human Bioscience
Duration: 3FT Hon
Entry Requirements: *GCE:* 260-280. *SQAH:* AAA-BBBB. *IB:* 24.
BTEC NC: DD. *BTEC ND:* DMM. *OCR ND:* D *OCR NED:* M2

D4B1 BA Heritage Management/Human Bioscience
Duration: 3FT Hon
Entry Requirements: *GCE:* 260-280. *SQAH:* AAA-BBBB. *IB:* 24.
BTEC NC: DD. *BTEC ND:* DMM. *OCR ND:* D *OCR NED:* M2

B1W4 BA Human Bioscience/Drama
Duration: 3FT Hon
Entry Requirements: *GCE:* 260-280. *SQAH:* AAA-BBBB. *IB:* 24.
BTEC NC: DD. *BTEC ND:* DMM. *OCR ND:* D *OCR NED:* M2
Interview required.

B1LX BA Human Bioscience/International Development
Duration: 3FT Hon
Entry Requirements: *GCE:* 260-280. *SQAH:* AAA-BBBB. *IB:* 24.
BTEC NC: DD. *BTEC ND:* DMM. *OCR ND:* D *OCR NED:* M2

L9B1 BA International Development/Human Bioscience
Duration: 3FT Hon
Entry Requirements: *GCE:* 260-280. *SQAH:* AAA-BBBB. *IB:* 24.
BTEC NC: DD. *BTEC ND:* DMM. *OCR ND:* D *OCR NED:* M2

M1B1 BA Law/Human Bioscience
Duration: 3FT Hon
Entry Requirements: *GCE:* 260-280. *SQAH:* AAA-BBBB. *IB:* 24.
BTEC NC: DD. *BTEC ND:* DMM. *OCR ND:* D *OCR NED:* M2

NB81 BA Leisure & Lifestyle Management/Human Bioscience
Duration: 3FT Hon
Entry Requirements: *GCE:* 260-280. *SQAH:* AAA-BBBB. *IB:* 24.
BTEC NC: DD. *BTEC ND:* DMM. *OCR ND:* D *OCR NED:* M2

N2B1 BA Management/Human Bioscience
Duration: 3FT Hon
Entry Requirements: *GCE:* 260-280. *SQAH:* AAA-BBBB. *IB:* 24.
BTEC NC: DD. *BTEC ND:* DMM. *OCR ND:* D *OCR NED:* M2

N5B1 BA Marketing/Human Bioscience
Duration: 3FT Hon
Entry Requirements: *GCE:* 260-280. *SQAH:* AAA-BBBB. *IB:* 24.
BTEC NC: DD. *BTEC ND:* DMM. *OCR ND:* D *OCR NED:* M2

P3B1 BA Media Production/Human Bioscience
Duration: 3FT Hon
Entry Requirements: *GCE:* 260-280. *SQAH:* AAA-BBBB. *IB:* 24.
BTEC NC: DD. *BTEC ND:* DMM. *OCR ND:* D *OCR NED:* M2

L2B1 BA Politics/Human Bioscience
Duration: 3FT Hon
Entry Requirements: *GCE:* 260-280. *SQAH:* AAA-BBBB. *IB:* 24.
BTEC NC: DD. *BTEC ND:* DMM. *OCR ND:* D *OCR NED:* M2

W3B1 BA Popular Music/Human Biology
Duration: 3FT Hon
Entry Requirements: *GCE:* 260-280. *SQAH:* AAA-BBBB. *IB:* 24.
BTEC NC: DD. *BTEC ND:* DMM. *OCR ND:* D *OCR NED:* M2
Interview required.

N2BC BA Social Enterprise Development/Human Bioscience
Duration: 3FT Hon
Entry Requirements: *GCE:* 260-280. *SQAH:* AAA-BBBB. *IB:* 24.
BTEC NC: DD. *BTEC ND:* DMM. *OCR ND:* D *OCR NED:* M2

L3B1 BA Sociology/Human Bioscience
Duration: 3FT Hon
Entry Requirements: *GCE:* 260-280. *SQAH:* AAA-BBBB. *IB:* 24.
BTEC NC: DD. *BTEC ND:* DMM. *OCR ND:* D *OCR NED:* M2

N8B1 BA Tourism/Human Bioscience
Duration: 3FT Hon
Entry Requirements: *GCE:* 260-280. *SQAH:* AAA-BBBB. *IB:* 24.
BTEC NC: DD. *BTEC ND:* DMM. *OCR ND:* D *OCR NED:* M2

C1B1 BSc Biological Conservation/Human Bioscience
Duration: 3FT Hon
Entry Requirements: *GCE:* 260-280. *SQAH:* AAA-BBBB. *IB:* 24.
BTEC NC: DD. *BTEC ND:* DMM. *OCR ND:* D *OCR NED:* M2

G5B1 BSc Business Computing Systems/Human Bioscience
Duration: 3FT Hon
Entry Requirements: *GCE:* 260-280. *SQAH:* AAA-BBBB. *IB:* 24.
BTEC NC: DD. *BTEC ND:* DMM. *OCR ND:* D *OCR NED:* M2

G4B1 BSc Computing/Human Bioscience
Duration: 3FT Hon
Entry Requirements: *GCE:* 260-280. *SQAH:* AAA-BBBB. *IB:* 24.
BTEC NC: DD. *BTEC ND:* DMM. *OCR ND:* D *OCR NED:* M2

B190 BSc Human Bioscience
Duration: 3FT Hon
Entry Requirements: *GCE:* 260-280. *SQAH:* AAA-BBBB. *IB:* 24.
BTEC NC: DD. *BTEC ND:* DMM. *OCR ND:* D *OCR NED:* M2

B1NG BSc Human Bioscience with Applied Management
Duration: 3FT Hon
Entry Requirements: *GCE:* 260-280. *SQAH:* AAA-BBBB. *IB:* 24.
BTEC NC: DD. *BTEC ND:* DMM. *OCR ND:* D *OCR NED:* M2

B1D4 BSc Human Bioscience with Equine Studies
Duration: 3FT Hon
Entry Requirements: *GCE:* 260-280. *SQAH:* AAA-BBBB. *IB:* 24.
BTEC NC: DD. *BTEC ND:* DMM. *OCR ND:* D *OCR NED:* M2

B1NM BSc Human Bioscience/Advertising
Duration: 3FT Hon
Entry Requirements: *GCE:* 260-280. *SQAH:* AAA-BBBB. *IB:* 24.
BTEC NC: DD. *BTEC ND:* DMM. *OCR ND:* D *OCR NED:* M2

B1C1 BSc Human Bioscience/Biological Conservation
Duration: 3FT Hon
Entry Requirements: *GCE:* 260-280. *SQAH:* AAA-BBBB. *IB:* 24.
BTEC NC: DD. *BTEC ND:* DMM. *OCR ND:* D *OCR NED:* M2

B1N1 BSc Human Bioscience/Business
Duration: 3FT Hon
Entry Requirements: *GCE:* 260-280. *SQAH:* AAA-BBBB. *IB:* 24.
BTEC NC: DD. *BTEC ND:* DMM. *OCR ND:* D *OCR NED:* M2

B1G5 BSc Human Bioscience/Business Computing Systems
Duration: 3FT Hon
Entry Requirements: *GCE:* 260-280. *SQAH:* AAA-BBBB. *IB:* 24.
BTEC NC: DD. *BTEC ND:* DMM. *OCR ND:* D *OCR NED:* M2

B1G4 BSc Human Bioscience/Computing
Duration: 3FT Hon
Entry Requirements: *GCE:* 260-280. *SQAH:* AAA-BBBB. *IB:* 24.
BTEC NC: DD. *BTEC ND:* DMM. *OCR ND:* D *OCR NED:* M2

B1W8 BSc Human Bioscience/Creative Writing
Duration: 3FT Hon
Entry Requirements: *GCE:* 260-280. *SQAH:* AAA-BBBB. *IB:* 24.
BTEC NC: DD. *BTEC ND:* DMM. *OCR ND:* D *OCR NED:* M2

B1L1 BSc Human Bioscience/Economics
Duration: 3FT Hon
Entry Requirements: *GCE:* 260-280. *SQAH:* AAA-BBBB. *IB:* 24.
BTEC NC: DD. *BTEC ND:* DMM. *OCR ND:* D *OCR NED:* M2

B1X3 BSc Human Bioscience/Education Studies
Duration: 3FT Hon
Entry Requirements: *GCE:* 260-280. *SQAH:* AAA-BBBB. *IB:* 24.
BTEC NC: DD. *BTEC ND:* DMM. *OCR ND:* D *OCR NED:* M2

B1Q3 BSc Human Bioscience/English
Duration: 3FT Hon
Entry Requirements: *GCE:* 260-280. *SQAH:* AAA-BBBB. *IB:* 24.
BTEC NC: DD. *BTEC ND:* DMM. *OCR ND:* D *OCR NED:* M2

B1NV BSc Human Bioscience/Events Management
Duration: 3FT Hon
Entry Requirements: *GCE:* 260-280. *SQAH:* AAA-BBBB. *IB:* 24.
BTEC NC: DD. *BTEC ND:* DMM. *OCR ND:* D *OCR NED:* M2

B1W6 BSc Human Bioscience/Film & Television Studies
Duration: 3FT Hon
Entry Requirements: *GCE:* 260-280. *SQAH:* AAA-BBBB. *IB:* 24.
BTEC NC: DD. *BTEC ND:* DMM. *OCR ND:* D *OCR NED:* M2

B1L4 BSc Human Bioscience/Health Studies
Duration: 3FT Hon
Entry Requirements: *GCE:* 260-280. *SQAH:* AAA-BBBB. *IB:* 24.
BTEC NC: DD. *BTEC ND:* DMM. *OCR ND:* D *OCR NED:* M2

B1DK BSc Human Bioscience/Heritage Management
Duration: 3FT Hon
Entry Requirements: *GCE:* 260-280. *SQAH:* AAA-BBBB. *IB:* 24.
BTEC NC: DD. *BTEC ND:* DMM. *OCR ND:* D *OCR NED:* M2

B1M1 BSc Human Bioscience/Law
Duration: 3FT Hon
Entry Requirements: *GCE:* 260-280. *SQAH:* AAA-BBBB. *IB:* 24.
BTEC NC: DD. *BTEC ND:* DMM. *OCR ND:* D *OCR NED:* M2

B1NW BSc Human Bioscience/Leisure & Lifestyle Management
Duration: 3FT Hon
Entry Requirements: *GCE:* 260-280. *SQAH:* AAA-BBBB. *IB:* 24.
BTEC NC: DD. *BTEC ND:* DMM. *OCR ND:* D *OCR NED:* M2

B1N2 BSc Human Bioscience/Management
Duration: 3FT Hon
Entry Requirements: *GCE:* 260-280. *SQAH:* AAA-BBBB. *IB:* 24.
BTEC NC: DD. *BTEC ND:* DMM. *OCR ND:* D *OCR NED:* M2

B1N5 BSc Human Bioscience/Marketing
Duration: 3FT Hon
Entry Requirements: *GCE:* 260-280. *SQAH:* AAA-BBBB. *IB:* 24.
BTEC NC: DD. *BTEC ND:* DMM. *OCR ND:* D *OCR NED:* M2

B1P3 BSc Human Bioscience/Media Production
Duration: 3FT Hon
Entry Requirements: *GCE:* 260-280. *SQAH:* AAA-BBBB. *IB:* 24.
BTEC NC: DD. *BTEC ND:* DMM. *OCR ND:* D *OCR NED:* M2

B1F8 BSc Human Bioscience/Physical Geography
Duration: 3FT Hon
Entry Requirements: *GCE:* 260-280. *SQAH:* AAA-BBBB. *IB:* 24.
BTEC NC: DD. *BTEC ND:* DMM. *OCR ND:* D *OCR NED:* M2

B1L2 BSc Human Bioscience/Politics
Duration: 3FT Hon
Entry Requirements: *GCE:* 260-280. *SQAH:* AAA-BBBB. *IB:* 24.
BTEC NC: DD. *BTEC ND:* DMM. *OCR ND:* D *OCR NED:* M2

B1W3 BSc Human Bioscience/Popular Music
Duration: 3FT Hon
Entry Requirements: *GCE:* 260-280. *SQAH:* AAA-BBBB. *IB:* 24.
BTEC NC: DD. *BTEC ND:* DMM. *OCR ND:* D *OCR NED:* M2
Interview required.

B1C8 BSc Human Bioscience/Psychology
Duration: 3FT Hon
Entry Requirements: *GCE:* 260-280. *SQAH:* AAA-BBBB. *IB:* 24.
BTEC NC: DD. *BTEC ND:* DMM. *OCR ND:* D *OCR NED:* M2

B1NA BSc Human Bioscience/Social Enterprise Development
Duration: 3FT Hon
Entry Requirements: *GCE:* 260-280. *SQAH:* AAA-BBBB. *IB:* 24.
BTEC NC: DD. *BTEC ND:* DMM. *OCR ND:* D *OCR NED:* M2

B1L3 BSc Human Bioscience/Sociology
Duration: 3FT Hon
Entry Requirements: *GCE:* 260-280. *SQAH:* AAA-BBBB. *IB:* 24.
BTEC NC: DD. *BTEC ND:* DMM. *OCR ND:* D *OCR NED:* M2

B1C6 BSc Human Bioscience/Sport Studies
Duration: 3FT Hon
Entry Requirements: *GCE:* 260-280. *SQAH:* AAA-BBBB. *IB:* 24.
BTEC NC: DD. *BTEC ND:* DMM. *OCR ND:* D *OCR NED:* M2

B1N8 BSc Human Bioscience/Tourism
Duration: 3FT Hon
Entry Requirements: *GCE:* 260-280. *SQAH:* AAA-BBBB. *IB:* 24.
BTEC NC: DD. *BTEC ND:* DMM. *OCR ND:* D *OCR NED:* M2

B1FV BSc Human Bioscience/Wastes Management
Duration: 3FT Hon
Entry Requirements: *GCE:* 260-280. *SQAH:* AAA-BBBB. *IB:* 24.
BTEC NC: DD. *BTEC ND:* DMM. *OCR ND:* D *OCR NED:* M2

B1GK BSc Human Bioscience/Web Design
Duration: 3FT Hon
Entry Requirements: *GCE:* 260-280. *SQAH:* AAA-BBBB. *IB:* 24.
BTEC NC: DD. *BTEC ND:* DMM. *OCR ND:* D *OCR NED:* M2

F8B1 BSc Physical Geography/Human Bioscience
Duration: 3FT Hon
Entry Requirements: *GCE:* 260-280. *SQAH:* AAA-BBBB. *IB:* 24.
BTEC NC: DD. *BTEC ND:* DMM. *OCR ND:* D *OCR NED:* M2

B985 BSc Podiatry
Duration: 3FT Hon   CRB Check: Required
Entry Requirements: *GCE:* 260-280. *SQAH:* AAA-BBBB. *IB:* 24.
BTEC NC: DD. *BTEC ND:* DMM. *OCR ND:* D *OCR NED:* M2
Interview required.

C8B1 BSc Psychology/Human Bioscience
Duration: 3FT Hon
Entry Requirements: *GCE:* 260-280. *SQAH:* AAA-BBBB. *IB:* 24.
BTEC NC: DD. *BTEC ND:* DMM. *OCR ND:* D *OCR NED:* M2

C6B1 BSc Sport Studies/Human Bioscience
Duration: 3FT Hon
Entry Requirements: *GCE:* 260-280. *SQAH:* AAA-BBBB. *IB:* 24.
BTEC NC: DD. *BTEC ND:* DMM. *OCR ND:* D *OCR NED:* M2

F8BD BSc Wastes Management/Human Bioscience
Duration: 3FT Hon
Entry Requirements: *GCE:* 260-280. *SQAH:* AAA-BBBB. *IB:* 24.
BTEC NC: DD. *BTEC ND:* DMM. *OCR ND:* D *OCR NED:* M2

G4BD BSc Web Design/Human Bioscience
Duration: 3FT Hon
Entry Requirements: *GCE:* 260-280. *SQAH:* AAA-BBBB. *IB:* 24.
BTEC NC: DD. *BTEC ND:* DMM. *OCR ND:* D *OCR NED:* M2

N77 NORTHUMBRIA UNIVERSITY
TRINITY BUILDING
NORTHUMBERLAND ROAD
NEWCASTLE UPON TYNE NE1 8ST
t: 0191 243 7420 f: 0191 227 4561
e: er.admissions@northumbria.ac.uk
// www.northumbria.ac.uk

B150 BSc Human Biosciences
Duration: 3FT/4SW Hon
Entry Requirements: *GCE:* 280. *SQAH:* BBCCC. *SQAAH:* BCC. *IB:* 25. *OCR ND:* M1 *OCR NED:* P1

B160 BSc Physiotherapy
Duration: 3FT Hon   CRB Check: Required
Entry Requirements: *SQAH:* BBBBB. *SQAAH:* BBB. *IB:* 27. *BTEC NC:* DD. *BTEC ND:* DDM. *OCR ND:* D *OCR NED:* D2 Interview required.

N84 THE UNIVERSITY OF NOTTINGHAM
THE ADMISSIONS OFFICE
THE UNIVERSITY OF NOTTINGHAM
UNIVERSITY PARK
NOTTINGHAM NG7 2RD
t: 0115 951 5151 f: 0115 951 4668
// www.nottingham.ac.uk

B140 BSc Neuroscience
Duration: 3FT Hon
Entry Requirements: *GCE:* ABB. *SQAAH:* BBB. *IB:* 34.

B1C7 BSc Neuroscience with Biochemistry
Duration: 3FT Hon
Entry Requirements: *GCE:* ABB. *SQAAH:* BBB. *IB:* 34.

B1B2 BSc Neuroscience with Pharmacology
Duration: 3FT Hon
Entry Requirements: *GCE:* ABB. *SQAAH:* ABB. *IB:* 34.

B160 BSc Physiotherapy
Duration: 3FT Hon   CRB Check: Required
Entry Requirements: *GCE:* ABB. *SQAAH:* BBB. *IB:* 32. *BTEC NC:* DM. *BTEC ND:* DDM. Interview required.

B141 MSci Neuroscience (4 years)
Duration: 4FT Hon
Entry Requirements: *GCE:* ABB. *SQAAH:* ABB. *IB:* 34.

O66 OXFORD BROOKES UNIVERSITY
ADMISSIONS OFFICE
HEADINGTON CAMPUS
GIPSY LANE
OXFORD OX3 0BP
t: 01865 483040 f: 01865 483983
e: admissions@brookes.ac.uk
// www.brookes.ac.uk

BLC6 BA/BSc Human Biosciences/Anthropology
Duration: 3FT Hon
Entry Requirements: Contact the institution for details.

BG13 BA/BSc Human Biosciences/Statistics
Duration: 3FT Hon
Entry Requirements: *GCE:* BCC. *BTEC ND:* MMM.

B190 BMedSci Medical Science
Duration: 3FT Hon
Entry Requirements: Contact the institution for details.

B150 BSc Human Biology
Duration: 3FT Hon
Entry Requirements: *GCE:* BBC.

BF17 BSc Human Biosciences/Environmental Sciences
Duration: 3FT Hon
Entry Requirements: Contact the institution for details.

BGC1 BSc Human Biosciences/Mathematics
Duration: 3FT Hon
Entry Requirements: Contact the institution for details.

BB14 BSc Human Biosciences/Nutrition
Duration: 3FT Hon
Entry Requirements: Contact the institution for details.

BCD8 BSc Human Biosciences/Psychology
Duration: 3FT Hon
Entry Requirements: Contact the institution for details.

BC16 BSc Human Biosciences/Sport & Exercise Science
Duration: 3FT Hon
Entry Requirements: Contact the institution for details.

B160 BSc Physiotherapy
Duration: 3FT Hon   CRB Check: Required
Entry Requirements: *GCE:* ABB. *SQAAH:* BBB.

P60 UNIVERSITY OF PLYMOUTH
DRAKE CIRCUS
PLYMOUTH PL4 8AA
t: 01752 588037 f: 01752 588050
e: admissions@plymouth.ac.uk
// www.plymouth.ac.uk

B160 BSc Physiotherapy
Duration: 3FT Hon   CRB Check: Required
Entry Requirements: *GCE:* 340. *IB:* 33. *BTEC NC:* DD. *BTEC ND:* DDD. *OCR ND:* D *OCR NED:* D1

B985 BSc Podiatry
Duration: 3FT Hon   CRB Check: Required
Entry Requirements: *GCE:* 240-260. *IB:* 27. *BTEC NC:* DD. *BTEC ND:* MMM. *OCR ND:* D *OCR NED:* M2

P80 UNIVERSITY OF PORTSMOUTH
ACADEMIC REGISTRY
UNIVERSITY HOUSE
WINSTON CHURCHILL AVENUE
PORTSMOUTH PO1 2UP
t: 023 9284 8484 f: 023 9284 3082
e: admissions@port.ac.uk
// www.port.ac.uk

B121 BSc Human Physiology
Duration: 3FT Hon
Entry Requirements: *GCE:* 240. *IB:* 26. *BTEC NC:* DD. *BTEC ND:* MMM. Interview required.

Q25 QUEEN MARGARET UNIVERSITY, EDINBURGH
QUEEN MARGARET UNIVERSITY DRIVE
EDINBURGH EH21 6UU
t: 0131474 0000 f: 0131 474 0001
e: admissions@qmu.ac.uk
// www.qmu.ac.uk

B160 BSc Physiotherapy
Duration: 4FT Hon   CRB Check: Required
Entry Requirements: *GCE:* 340. *IB:* 32.

B985 BSc Podiatry
Duration: 4FT Hon   CRB Check: Required
Entry Requirements: *GCE:* 240. *IB:* 28.

Q75 QUEEN'S UNIVERSITY BELFAST
UNIVERSITY ROAD
BELFAST BT7 1NN
t: 028 9097 3838 f: 028 9097 5151
e: admissions@qub.ac.uk
// www.qub.ac.uk

B100 BSc Human Biology
Duration: 3FT Hon
Entry Requirements: *GCE:* ABB-BBBb. *IB:* 33.

R36 ROBERT GORDON UNIVERSITY
ROBERT GORDON UNIVERSITY
SCHOOLHILL
ABERDEEN
SCOTLAND AB10 1FR
t: 01224 26 27 28 f: 01224 26 21 47
e: UGOffice@rgu.ac.uk
// www.rgu.ac.uk

B160 BSc Physiotherapy
Duration: 4FT Hon   CRB Check: Required
Entry Requirements: *GCE:* 300. *SQAH:* ABBC-BBBB. *IB:* 32.
Interview required.

S03 THE UNIVERSITY OF SALFORD
SALFORD M5 4WT
t: 0161 295 4545 f: 0161 295 4646
e: ug-admissions@salford.ac.uk
// www.salford.ac.uk

BC15 BSc Human Biology and Infectious Diseases
Duration: 3FT Hon
Entry Requirements: *GCE:* 240. *IB:* 28. *BTEC NC:* DD. *BTEC ND:* MPP.

B160 BSc Physiotherapy
Duration: 3FT Hon   CRB Check: Required
Entry Requirements: *GCE:* 300. *SQAH:* AABBB. *SQAAH:* BBB. *IB:* 32. *BTEC ND:* DDM. Interview required.

B985 BSc Podiatry
Duration: 3FT Hon   CRB Check: Required
Entry Requirements: *GCE:* 240. *SQAH:* BCCCC. *SQAAH:* CCC. *IB:* 24. *BTEC NC:* DD. *BTEC ND:* MMM. Interview required.

S21 SHEFFIELD HALLAM UNIVERSITY
CITY CAMPUS
HOWARD STREET
SHEFFIELD S1 1WB
t: 0114 225 5555 f: 0114 225 2167
e: admissions@shu.ac.uk
// www.shu.ac.uk

B160 BSc Physiotherapy
Duration: 3FT Hon
Entry Requirements: *GCE:* 320.

S27 UNIVERSITY OF SOUTHAMPTON
HIGHFIELD
SOUTHAMPTON SO17 1BJ
t: 023 8059 4732 f: 023 8059 3037
e: admissions@soton.ac.uk
// www.southampton.ac.uk

CB71 BSc Biochemistry/BiomedicalSc/Pharmacology with Foundation year (4 years)
Duration: 4FT Hon
Entry Requirements: *GCE:* BBB. *IB:* 30.

B120 BSc Healthcare Science (Cardiovascular)
Duration: 3FT Hon   CRB Check: Required
Entry Requirements: Contact the institution for details.

B121 BSc Healthcare Science (Respiratory and Sleep Sciences)
Duration: 3FT Hon   CRB Check: Required
Entry Requirements: Contact the institution for details.

B160 BSc Physiotherapy
Duration: 3FT Hon   CRB Check: Required
Entry Requirements: *GCE:* ABBb. *IB:* 33.

F1BC MChem Chemistry with Medicinal Science (4 years)
Duration: 4FT Hon
Entry Requirements: *GCE:* AAB-ABB. *SQAH:* AABBB. *SQAAH:* ABB. *IB:* 34. Interview required.

S36 UNIVERSITY OF ST ANDREWS
ST KATHARINE'S WEST
16 THE SCORES
ST ANDREWS
FIFE KY16 9AX
t: 01334 462150 f: 01334 463330
e: admissions@st-andrews.ac.uk
// www.st-andrews.ac.uk

B140 BSc Neuroscience
Duration: 4FT Hon
Entry Requirements: *GCE:* AAB. *SQAH:* AABB. *IB:* 35.

S49 ST GEORGE'S, UNIVERSITY OF LONDON
CRANMER TERRACE
LONDON SW17 0RE
t: +44 (0)20 8725 2333 f: +44 (0)20 8725 0841
e: enquiries@sgul.ac.uk
// www.sgul.ac.uk

B160 BSc Physiotherapy
Duration: 3FT Hon   CRB Check: Required
Entry Requirements: *GCE:* 320. Interview required.

B120 BSc (Hons) Healthcare Science (Physiological Sciences)
Duration: 3FT Hon **CRB Check:** Required
Entry Requirements: Interview required.

S72 STAFFORDSHIRE UNIVERSITY
COLLEGE ROAD
STOKE ON TRENT ST4 2DE
t: 01782 292753 f: 01782 292740
e: admissions@staffs.ac.uk
// www.staffs.ac.uk

B150 BSc Human Biology
Duration: 3FT Hon
Entry Requirements: *GCE:* 200-260. *IB:* 24. *BTEC NC:* DM.
BTEC ND: DMM.

BC18 BSc Human Biology and Psychology
Duration: 3FT Hon
Entry Requirements: *GCE:* 200-260. *IB:* 24. *BTEC NC:* DM.
BTEC ND: DMM.

S84 UNIVERSITY OF SUNDERLAND
STUDENT HELPLINE
THE STUDENT GATEWAY
CHESTER ROAD
SUNDERLAND SR1 3SD
t: 0191 515 3000 f: 0191 515 3805
e: student.helpline@sunderland.ac.uk
// www.sunderland.ac.uk

B120 BSc Physiological Sciences
Duration: 3FT Hon
Entry Requirements: *IB:* 24.

S85 UNIVERSITY OF SURREY
STAG HILL
GUILDFORD
SURREY GU2 7XH
t: +44(0)1483 689305 f: +44(0)1483 689388
e: ugteam@surrey.ac.uk
// www.surrey.ac.uk

C7B1 BSc Biochemistry (Neuroscience) (3 or 4 years)
Duration: 3FT/4SW Hon
Entry Requirements: *GCE:* AAB-ABB. *SQAH:* AABBB-ABBBB. *BTEC ND:* DDD. Interview required.

S90 UNIVERSITY OF SUSSEX
UNDERGRADUATE ADMISSIONS
SUSSEX HOUSE
UNIVERSITY OF SUSSEX
BRIGHTON BN1 9RH
t: 01273 678416 f: 01273 678545
e: ug.applicants@sussex.ac.uk
// www.sussex.ac.uk

B142 BSc Medical Neuroscience
Duration: 3FT Hon
Entry Requirements: *GCE:* AAB-ABB. *SQAH:* AAABB-AABBB. *BTEC NC:* DM. *BTEC ND:* DDM. *OCR ND:* M1

B140 BSc Neuroscience
Duration: 3FT Hon
Entry Requirements: *GCE:* AAB-ABB. *SQAH:* AAABB-AABBB. *BTEC NC:* DM. *BTEC ND:* DDM. *OCR ND:* M1 *OCR NED:* D2

CB81 BSc Psychology with Neuroscience
Duration: 3FT Hon
Entry Requirements: *GCE:* AAB. *SQAH:* AAABB. *IB:* 36. *BTEC NC:* DM. *BTEC ND:* DDD. *OCR ND:* D *OCR NED:* D1

S93 SWANSEA UNIVERSITY
SINGLETON PARK
SWANSEA SA2 8PP
t: 01792 295111 f: 01792 295110
e: admissions@swansea.ac.uk
// www.swansea.ac.uk

B1B8 BSc Clinical Physiology with Cardiology
Duration: 4FT Hon **CRB Check:** Required
Entry Requirements: *GCE:* BBB. *BTEC ND:* DDD. Interview required.

B121 BSc Clinical Physiology with Respiratory Physiology
Duration: 4FT Hon **CRB Check:** Required
Entry Requirements: *GCE:* BBB. *BTEC ND:* DDD. Interview required.

T20 TEESSIDE UNIVERSITY
MIDDLESBROUGH TS1 3BA
t: 01642 218121 f: 01642 384201
e: registry@tees.ac.uk
// www.tees.ac.uk

BF14 BSc Crime Scene Science
Duration: 3FT/4SW Hon
Entry Requirements: *GCE:* 280-300. *IB:* 30. *BTEC NC:* MM. *BTEC ND:* DMM. Interview required.

B160 BSc Physiotherapy
Duration: 3FT Hon **CRB Check:** Required
Entry Requirements: *GCE:* 300. *BTEC NC:* DM. *BTEC ND:* DDM. *OCR ND:* M1 *OCR NED:* D2 Interview required.

U20 UNIVERSITY OF ULSTER
COLERAINE
CO. LONDONDERRY
NORTHERN IRELAND BT52 1SA
t: 028 7032 4221 f: 028 7032 4908
e: online@ulster.ac.uk
// www.ulster.ac.uk

B120 BSc Clinical Physiology (Cardiology)
Duration: 4SW Hon   CRB Check: Required
Entry Requirements: *GCE:* 280. *IB:* 24. *BTEC NC:* MM. *BTEC ND:* DMM.

B121 BSc Clinical Physiology (Respiratory)
Duration: 4SW Hon   CRB Check: Required
Entry Requirements: *GCE:* 280. *IB:* 24. *BTEC NC:* MM. *BTEC ND:* DMM.

B160 BSc Physiotherapy
Duration: 3FT Hon   CRB Check: Required
Entry Requirements: *GCE:* BBB. *SQAH:* AABCC. *SQAAH:* BBB. *IB:* 25. *BTEC NC:* DD. *BTEC ND:* DDD. Admissions Test required.

B985 BSc Podiatry
Duration: 3FT Hon   CRB Check: Required
Entry Requirements: *GCE:* BBB. *SQAH:* AABCC. *SQAAH:* BBB. *IB:* 25. *BTEC NC:* MM. *BTEC ND:* DDM. Admissions Test required.

U80 UNIVERSITY COLLEGE LONDON (UNIVERSITY OF LONDON)
GOWER STREET
LONDON WC1E 6BT
t: 020 7679 3000 f: 020 7679 3001
// www.ucl.ac.uk

B190 BSc Bioprocessing of New Medicines (Science and Engineering)
Duration: 3FT Hon
Entry Requirements: *GCE:* AABe-ABBe. *SQAAH:* AAB-ABB. *BTEC ND:* DDD. Interview required.

B140 BSc Neuroscience
Duration: 3FT Hon
Entry Requirements: *GCE:* AAAe-AABe. *SQAAH:* AAA-AAB. Interview required.

B141 MSci Neuroscience
Duration: 4FT Hon
Entry Requirements: *GCE:* AAAe-AABe. *SQAAH:* AAA-AAB. Interview required.

W50 UNIVERSITY OF WESTMINSTER
2ND FLOOR
101 NEW CAVENDISH STREET,
LONDON W1W 6XH
t: 020 7911 5000 f: 020 7911 5788
e: course-enquiries@westminster.ac.uk
// www.westminster.ac.uk

B140 BSc Cognitive Neuroscience
Duration: 3FT Hon
Entry Requirements: *GCE:* BBB. *SQAH:* CCCC. *IB:* 26. *BTEC ND:* MMM. Interview required.

BB12 BSc Physiology and Pharmacology
Duration: 3FT Hon
Entry Requirements: *GCE:* CCD. *SQAH:* CCCC. *IB:* 26. *BTEC NC:* DM. *BTEC ND:* MMM. Interview required.

BBC2 BSc Physiology and Pharmacology with Foundation
Duration: 4FT Hon
Entry Requirements: *GCE:* CCD. *SQAH:* CCCC. *IB:* 26. *BTEC NC:* DM. *BTEC ND:* MMP. Interview required.

W67 WIGAN AND LEIGH COLLEGE
PO BOX 53
PARSONS WALK
WIGAN WN1 1RS
t: 01942 761605 f: 01942 760223
// www.wigan-leigh.ac.uk

B160 FdSc Spa Therapy
Duration: 2FT Fdg
Entry Requirements: Contact the institution for details.

W75 UNIVERSITY OF WOLVERHAMPTON
ADMISSIONS UNIT
MX207, CAMP STREET
WOLVERHAMPTON
WEST MIDLANDS WV1 1AD
t: 01902 321000 f: 01902 321896
e: admissions@wlv.ac.uk
// www.wlv.ac.uk

B120 BSc Healthcare Science (Physiological Sciences)
Duration: 3FT/4SW Hon
Entry Requirements: *GCE:* 220-240. *IB:* 30.

W80 UNIVERSITY OF WORCESTER
HENWICK GROVE
WORCESTER WR2 6AJ
t: 01905 855111 f: 01905 855377
e: admissions@worc.ac.uk
// www.worcester.ac.uk

B150 BSc Human Biology
Duration: 3FT Hon
Entry Requirements: *Foundation:* Merit. *GCE:* 220-240. *IB:* 24.
BTEC NC: DD. *BTEC ND:* MMM. *OCR ND:* D *OCR NED:* M3

Y75 YORK ST JOHN UNIVERSITY
LORD MAYOR'S WALK
YORK YO31 7EX
t: 01904 876598 f: 01904 876940/876921
e: admissions@yorksj.ac.uk
// w3.yorksj.ac.uk

B160 BSc Physiotherapy
Duration: 3FT Hon   CRB Check: Required
Entry Requirements: *GCE:* 300. *IB:* 30. *OCR ND:* D Interview required.

PHARMACOLOGY, TOXICOLOGY AND PHARMACY

A20 THE UNIVERSITY OF ABERDEEN
UNIVERSITY OFFICE
KING'S COLLEGE
ABERDEEN AB24 3FX
t: +44 (0) 1224 273504 f: +44 (0) 1224 272034
e: sras@abdn.ac.uk
// www.abdn.ac.uk/sras

B9B2 BSc Biomedical Science (Pharmacology)
Duration: 4FT Hon
Entry Requirements: *GCE:* ABB. *SQAH:* AABB. *IB:* 32. *BTEC ND:* DDD.

BC25 BSc Immunology and Pharmacology
Duration: 4FT Hon
Entry Requirements: *GCE:* 240. *SQAH:* BBBB. *SQAAH:* BCC. *IB:* 28. *BTEC ND:* MMM.

B210 BSc Pharmacology
Duration: 4FT Hon
Entry Requirements: *GCE:* 240. *SQAH:* BBBB. *SQAAH:* BCC. *IB:* 28. *BTEC ND:* MMM.

B9BF MSci Biomedical Science (Pharmacology) with Industrial Placement
Duration: 5FT Hon
Entry Requirements: *GCE:* ABB. *SQAH:* AABB. *IB:* 32. *BTEC ND:* DDD.

BC2M MSci Immunology and Pharmacology with Industrial Placement
Duration: 5FT Hon
Entry Requirements: *GCE:* ABB. *SQAH:* AABB. *IB:* 32. *BTEC ND:* DDD.

B211 MSci Pharmacology with Industrial Placement
Duration: 5FT Hon
Entry Requirements: *GCE:* ABB. *SQAH:* AABB. *IB:* 32. *BTEC ND:* DDD.

A80 ASTON UNIVERSITY, BIRMINGHAM
ASTON TRIANGLE
BIRMINGHAM B4 7ET
t: 0121 204 4444 f: 0121 204 3696
e: admissions@aston.ac.uk
// www.aston.ac.uk

B230 MPharm Pharmacy
Duration: 4FT Hon   CRB Check: Required
Entry Requirements: *GCE:* AAB-ABB. *SQAH:* AABBB. *SQAAH:* ABB. *IB:* 34. *BTEC NC:* DD. *BTEC ND:* DDD.

B16 UNIVERSITY OF BATH
CLAVERTON DOWN
BATH BA2 7AY
t: 01225 383019 f: 01225 386366
e: admissions@bath.ac.uk
// www.bath.ac.uk

B210 BSc Pharmacology
Duration: 3FT Hon
Entry Requirements: *GCE:* ABB. *SQAAH:* AAB. *IB:* 34. Interview required.

B230 MPharm Pharmacy
Duration: 4FT Hon
Entry Requirements: *GCE:* AAB. *SQAAH:* AAA. *IB:* 36. Interview required.

B213 MPharmacol Pharmacology
Duration: 4SW Hon
Entry Requirements: *GCE:* ABB. *SQAAH:* AAB. *IB:* 34. Interview required.

B32 THE UNIVERSITY OF BIRMINGHAM
EDGBASTON
BIRMINGHAM B15 2TT
t: 0121 415 8900 f: 0121 414 7159
e: admissions@bham.ac.uk
// www.bham.ac.uk

F1B2 BSc Chemistry with Pharmacology
Duration: 3FT Hon
Entry Requirements: *GCE:* BBB. *SQAH:* BBBBB-BBBBC. *SQAAH:* BB.

F1BG MSci Chemistry with Pharmacology
Duration: 4FT Hon
Entry Requirements: *GCE:* ABB-BBB. *SQAH:* AABBB-BBBBC. *SQAAH:* AB-BB.

B56 THE UNIVERSITY OF BRADFORD
RICHMOND ROAD
BRADFORD
WEST YORKSHIRE BD7 1DP
t: 0800 073 1225 f: 01274 235585
e: course-enquiries@bradford.ac.uk
// www.bradford.ac.uk

F1B2 BSc Chemistry with Pharmaceutical and Forensic Science
Duration: 3FT Hon
Entry Requirements: *GCE:* 260. *IB:* 24.

F1BF BSc Chemistry with Pharmaceutical and Forensic Science (4 years)
Duration: 4SW Hon
Entry Requirements: *GCE:* 260. *IB:* 24.

B2N2 BSc Pharmaceutical Management
Duration: 3FT Hon
Entry Requirements: *GCE:* 240. *IB:* 24.

B210 BSc Pharmacology
Duration: 3FT Hon
Entry Requirements: *GCE:* 260. *IB:* 24. Interview required.

F1BG MChem Chemistry with Pharmaceutical and Forensic Science (4 years)
Duration: 4FT Hon
Entry Requirements: *GCE:* 260. *IB:* 24.

B230 MPharm Pharmacy (4 years)
Duration: 4FT Hon   CRB Check: Required
Entry Requirements: *GCE:* 300. *IB:* 32. *BTEC NC:* DM. *BTEC ND:* MMP. Interview required.

B231 MPharm Pharmacy (5 years practice-integrated programme)
Duration: 5SW Hon   CRB Check: Required
Entry Requirements: *GCE:* 300. *IB:* 30. *BTEC NC:* DM. *BTEC ND:* MMP. Interview required.

B72 UNIVERSITY OF BRIGHTON
209 MITHRAS HOUSE
LEWES ROAD
BRIGHTON BN2 4AT
t: 01273 644644 f: 01273 642607
e: admissions@brighton.ac.uk
// www.brighton.ac.uk

FB12 BSc Pharmaceutical and Chemical Sciences
Duration: 3FT Hon
Entry Requirements: *GCE:* BBC. *IB:* 28. *BTEC ND:* DMM.

LB52 FdSc Substance Misuse Intervention Strategies
Duration: 2FT Fdg
Entry Requirements: Contact the institution for details.

B230 MPharm Pharmacy (4 years)
Duration: 4FT Hon
Entry Requirements: *GCE:* ABB. *IB:* 32. *BTEC ND:* DDM.

B78 UNIVERSITY OF BRISTOL
UNDERGRADUATE ADMISSIONS OFFICE
SENATE HOUSE
TYNDALL AVENUE
BRISTOL BS8 1TH
t: 0117 928 9000 f: 0117 925 1424
e: ug-admissions@bristol.ac.uk
// www.bristol.ac.uk

B210 BSc Pharmacology
Duration: 3FT/4SW Hon
Entry Requirements: *GCE:* ABB. *SQAH:* AABBB. *SQAAH:* AB. *IB:* 33. *BTEC ND:* DDM.

B211 MSci Pharmacology with Study in Industry
Duration: 4FT Hon
Entry Requirements: *GCE:* ABB. *SQAH:* AABBB. *SQAAH:* AB. *IB:* 33. *BTEC ND:* DDM.

B80 UNIVERSITY OF THE WEST OF ENGLAND, BRISTOL
FRENCHAY CAMPUS
COLDHARBOUR LANE
BRISTOL BS16 1QY
t: +44 (0)117 32 83333 f: +44 (0)117 32 82810
e: admissions@uwe.ac.uk
// www.uwe.ac.uk

B201 BSc Substance Misuse (Top-up)
Duration: 1FT Hon
Entry Requirements: Contact the institution for details.

C15 CARDIFF UNIVERSITY
PO BOX 927
30-36 NEWPORT ROAD
CARDIFF CF24 0DE
t: 029 2087 9999 f: 029 2087 6138
e: admissions@cardiff.ac.uk
// www.cardiff.ac.uk

B210 BSc Medical Pharmacology
Duration: 3FT Hon
Entry Requirements: *GCE:* ABB. *SQAH:* AAABB. *SQAAH:* AAB-ABB.
IB: 34. *BTEC NC:* DD. *BTEC ND:* DDD. Interview required.

B230 MPharm Pharmacy
Duration: 4FT Hon
Entry Requirements: *GCE:* AAB. *SQAH:* AAABB. *SQAAH:* AAB. *IB:*
34. Interview required.

C30 UNIVERSITY OF CENTRAL LANCASHIRE
PRESTON
LANCS PR1 2HE
t: 01772 201201 f: 01772 894954
e: uadmissions@uclan.ac.uk
// www.uclan.ac.uk

B230 MPharm Pharmacy
Duration: 4FT Hon   CRB Check: Required
Entry Requirements: *GCE:* BBB. *SQAH:* ABBBB-BBBBB. *SQAAH:*
BBC-CCC. *IB:* 32. *BTEC NC:* DM. *BTEC ND:* DDM. *OCR ND:* M1
Interview required.

C85 COVENTRY UNIVERSITY
THE STUDENT CENTRE
COVENTRY UNIVERSITY
1 GULSON RD
COVENTRY CV1 2JH
t: 024 7615 2222 f: 024 7615 2223
e: studentenquiries@coventry.ac.uk
// www.coventry.ac.uk

BB92 BSc Medical and Pharmacological Sciences
Duration: 3FT/4SW Hon
Entry Requirements: *GCE:* CCC. *SQAH:* CCCCC. *IB:* 27. *BTEC ND:*
MMM. *OCR NED:* M3

D26 DE MONTFORT UNIVERSITY
THE GATEWAY
LEICESTER LE1 9BH
t: 0116 255 1551 f: 0116 250 6204
e: enquiries@dmu.ac.uk
// www.dmu.ac.uk

B204 BSc Pharmaceutical & Cosmetic Science
Duration: 3FT/4SW Hon
Entry Requirements: *GCE:* 280. *IB:* 28. *BTEC ND:* DMM. *OCR*
NED: M2

B230 MPharm Pharmacy (4 years)
Duration: 4FT Hon   CRB Check: Required
Entry Requirements: *GCE:* 320. *IB:* 30. *BTEC ND:* DDM. *OCR*
NED: D2 Interview required. Admissions Test required.

D65 UNIVERSITY OF DUNDEE
NETHERGATE
DUNDEE DD1 4HN
t: 01382 383838 f: 01382 388150
e: contactus@dundee.ac.uk
// www.dundee.ac.uk/admissions/
undergraduate/

B210 BSc Pharmacology
Duration: 4FT Hon
Entry Requirements: *GCE:* BBB. *SQAH:* ABBB. *IB:* 30. *BTEC ND:*
DDM.

E14 UNIVERSITY OF EAST ANGLIA
NORWICH NR4 7TJ
t: 01603 591515 f: 01603 458596
e: admissions@uea.ac.uk
// www.uea.ac.uk

B230 MPharm Pharmacy
Duration: 4FT Hon   CRB Check: Required
Entry Requirements: *GCE:* AAA-AAB. *SQAH:* AAAAA. *SQAAH:* AAA.
IB: 34. Interview required.

E28 UNIVERSITY OF EAST LONDON
DOCKLANDS CAMPUS
UNIVERSITY WAY
LONDON E16 2RD
t: 020 8223 3333 f: 020 8223 2978
e: study@uel.ac.uk
// www.uel.ac.uk

M9B2 BA Criminology with Toxicology
Duration: 3FT Hon
Entry Requirements: *GCE:* 240. *IB:* 28. *BTEC NC:* DD. *BTEC ND:*
MMM.

B290 BA Pharmacology with Toxicology
Duration: 3FT Hon
Entry Requirements: *GCE:* 200. *IB:* 24. *BTEC NC:* DM. *BTEC ND:* MMP.

BL26 BA/BSc Pharmacology/Anthropology
Duration: 3FT Hon
Entry Requirements: *GCE:* 200. *IB:* 24. *BTEC NC:* DM. *BTEC ND:* MMP.

BL29 BA/BSc Pharmacology/Third World Development
Duration: 3FT Hon
Entry Requirements: *GCE:* 200. *IB:* 24. *BTEC NC:* DM. *BTEC ND:* MMP.

C7B2 BSc Biochemistry with Pharmacology
Duration: 3FT Hon
Entry Requirements: *GCE:* 200. *IB:* 24. *BTEC NC:* DM. *BTEC ND:* MMP.

FB42 BSc Forensic Science and Toxicology
Duration: 3FT Hon
Entry Requirements: Contact the institution for details.

F4B2 BSc Forensic Science with Toxicology
Duration: 3FT Hon
Entry Requirements: *GCE:* 200. *IB:* 24. *BTEC NC:* DM. *BTEC ND:* MMP. *OCR ND:* M1 *OCR NED:* P1

C5B2 BSc Immunology with Toxicology
Duration: 3FT Hon
Entry Requirements: *GCE:* 200. *IB:* 24. *BTEC NC:* DM. *BTEC ND:* MMP. *OCR ND:* M1 *OCR NED:* P1

J7B2 BSc Medical Biotechnology with Pharmacology
Duration: 3FT Hon
Entry Requirements: Contact the institution for details.

B210 BSc Pharmacology
Duration: 3FT/4SW Hon
Entry Requirements: *GCE:* 200. *IB:* 24.

B291 BSc Pharmacology and Toxicology
Duration: 3FT Hon
Entry Requirements: Contact the institution for details.

B2C7 BSc Pharmacology with Biochemistry
Duration: 3FT Hon
Entry Requirements: *GCE:* 200. *IB:* 24. *BTEC NC:* DM. *BTEC ND:* MMP. *OCR ND:* M1 *OCR NED:* P1

B2M9 BSc Pharmacology with Criminology
Duration: 3FT Hon
Entry Requirements: *GCE:* 200. *IB:* 24. *BTEC NC:* DM. *BTEC ND:* MMP.

B2N2 BSc Pharmacology with Health Services Management
Duration: 3FT Hon
Entry Requirements: *GCE:* 200. *IB:* 24. *BTEC NC:* DM. *BTEC ND:* MMP.

B2C5 BSc Pharmacology with Medical Microbiology
Duration: 3FT Hon
Entry Requirements: *GCE:* 200. *IB:* 24. *BTEC NC:* DM. *BTEC ND:* MMP. *OCR ND:* M1 *OCR NED:* P1

B220 BSc Toxicology
Duration: 3FT/4SW Hon
Entry Requirements: *GCE:* 200. *IB:* 24.

B2B9 BSc Toxicology with Clinical Science
Duration: 3FT Hon
Entry Requirements: *GCE:* 200. *IB:* 24. *BTEC NC:* DM. *BTEC ND:* MMP.

B2MX BSc Toxicology with Criminology
Duration: 3FT Hon
Entry Requirements: *GCE:* 200. *IB:* 24. *BTEC NC:* DM. *BTEC ND:* MMP.

B2F4 BSc Toxicology with Forensic Science
Duration: 3FT Hon
Entry Requirements: *GCE:* 200. *IB:* 24. *BTEC NC:* DM. *BTEC ND:* MMP. *OCR ND:* M1 *OCR NED:* P1

B2G5 BSc Toxicology with Information Technology
Duration: 3FT Hon
Entry Requirements: *GCE:* 200. *IB:* 24. *BTEC NC:* DM. *BTEC ND:* MMP.

B2M1 BSc Toxicology with Law
Duration: 3FT Hon
Entry Requirements: *GCE:* 200. *IB:* 24.

BB29 BSc Toxicology/Clinical Science
Duration: 3FT Hon
Entry Requirements: *GCE:* 200. *IB:* 24. *BTEC NC:* DM. *BTEC ND:* MMP.

E56 THE UNIVERSITY OF EDINBURGH
STUDENT RECRUITMENT & ADMISSIONS
57 GEORGE SQUARE
EDINBURGH EH8 9JU
t: 0131 650 4360 f: 0131 651 1236
e: sra.enquiries@ed.ac.uk
// www.ed.ac.uk/studying/undergraduate/

B210 BSc Pharmacology
Duration: 4FT Hon
Entry Requirements: *GCE:* AAA-ABB. *SQAH:* AAAA-ABBB.

G28 UNIVERSITY OF GLASGOW
THE UNIVERSITY OF GLASGOW
THE FRASER BUILDING
65 HILLHEAD STREET
GLASGOW G12 8QF
t: 0141 330 6062 f: 0141 330 2961
e: student.recruitment@glasgow.ac.uk
// www.glasgow.ac.uk

B210 BSc Pharmacology
Duration: 4FT Hon
Entry Requirements: *GCE:* ABB. *SQAH:* AAAB-BBBB. *IB:* 32. *BTEC ND:* DDM.

B211 BSc Pharmacology (Faster Route)
Duration: 3FT Hon
Entry Requirements: *GCE:* AAA. *SQAAH:* AAA. *IB:* 38.

G42 GLASGOW CALEDONIAN UNIVERSITY
STUDENT RECRUITMENT & ADMISSIONS SERVICE
CITY CAMPUS
COWCADDENS ROAD
GLASGOW G4 0BA
t: 0141 331 3000 f: 0141 331 8676
e: undergraduate@gcu.ac.uk
// www.gcu.ac.uk

B210 BSc Pharmacology
Duration: 4FT Hon
Entry Requirements: *GCE:* BCC. *SQAH:* AAA-BBBC. *IB:* 24.

G70 UNIVERSITY OF GREENWICH
GREENWICH CAMPUS
OLD ROYAL NAVAL COLLEGE
PARK ROW
LONDON SE10 9LS
t: 0800 005 006 f: 020 8331 8145
e: courseinfo@gre.ac.uk
// www.gre.ac.uk

B202 BSc Pharmaceutical Sciences
Duration: 3FT Hon
Entry Requirements: *GCE:* 220. *IB:* 24.

B203 FdSc Pharmaceutical Science
Duration: 2FT Fdg
Entry Requirements: Contact the institution for details.

H36 UNIVERSITY OF HERTFORDSHIRE
UNIVERSITY ADMISSIONS SERVICE
COLLEGE LANE
HATFIELD
HERTS AL10 9AB
t: 01707 284800
// www.herts.ac.uk

B202 BSc Pharmaceutical Science
Duration: 3FT/4SW Hon
Entry Requirements: *GCE:* 240.

B208 BSc Pharmaceutical Science (Extended)
Duration: 4FT/5SW Hon
Entry Requirements: *GCE:* 80.

B205 BSc Pharmaceutical Science with a year in Europe
Duration: 4FT Hon
Entry Requirements: *GCE:* 260.

B203 BSc Pharmaceutical Science with a year in North America
Duration: 4FT Hon
Entry Requirements: *GCE:* 260.

B210 BSc Pharmacology
Duration: 3FT/4SW Hon
Entry Requirements: *GCE:* 260.

B211 BSc Pharmacology with a year in Europe
Duration: 4FT Hon
Entry Requirements: *GCE:* 260.

B212 BSc Pharmacology with a year in North America
Duration: 4FT Hon
Entry Requirements: *GCE:* 260.

B230 MPharm Pharmacy
Duration: 4FT Hon   CRB Check: Required
Entry Requirements: *GCE:* 320. *IB:* 27. *BTEC ND:* DDM. Interview required.

H60 THE UNIVERSITY OF HUDDERSFIELD
QUEENSGATE
HUDDERSFIELD HD1 3DH
t: 01484 473969 f: 01484 472765
e: admissionsandrecords@hud.ac.uk
// www.hud.ac.uk

B202 BSc Pharmaceutical Science
Duration: 3FT Hon
Entry Requirements: *GCE:* 220. *SQAH:* BBB. *IB:* 26. *BTEC ND:* MMP. Interview required.

B230 MPharm Pharmacy
Duration: 4FT Hon
Entry Requirements: *GCE:* 300. *BTEC NC:* DM. *BTEC ND:* DDM. Interview required.

B203 MSci Pharmaceutical Science
Duration: 4FT Hon
Entry Requirements: *GCE:* 160-280. *SQAH:* BBB. *IB:* 26. Interview required.

H72 THE UNIVERSITY OF HULL
THE UNIVERSITY OF HULL
COTTINGHAM ROAD
HULL HU6 7RX
t: 01482 466100 f: 01482 442290
e: admissions@hull.ac.uk
// www.hull.ac.uk

F1B2 BSc Chemistry with Forensic Science and Toxicology
Duration: 3FT Hon
Entry Requirements: *GCE:* 280-300. *IB:* 30. *BTEC ND:* DDM.

FBC2 BSc Pharmaceutical Science
Duration: 3FT Hon
Entry Requirements: *GCE:* 280-300. *IB:* 30. *BTEC ND:* DDM.

F1BF MChem Chemistry with Forensic Science and Toxicology
Duration: 4FT Hon
Entry Requirements: *GCE:* 280-300. *IB:* 30. *BTEC ND:* DDM.

F1BG MChem Chemistry with Forensic Science and Toxicology (with Industrial Experience)
Duration: 4FT Hon
Entry Requirements: *GCE:* 280-300. *IB:* 30. *BTEC ND:* DDM.

FB12 MPharmSci Pharmaceutical Science
Duration: 4FT Hon
Entry Requirements: *GCE:* 280-300. *IB:* 30. *BTEC ND:* DDM.

FB1F MPharmSci Pharmaceutical Science (Industrial Option)
Duration: 4FT Hon
Entry Requirements: *GCE:* 280-300. *IB:* 30. *BTEC ND:* DDM.

K12 KEELE UNIVERSITY
STAFFS ST5 5BG
t: 01782 734005 f: 01782 632343
e: undergraduate@keele.ac.uk
// www.keele.ac.uk

B231 BSc Pharmacy with Health Foundation Year
Duration: 5FT Deg   CRB Check: Required
Entry Requirements: *GCE:* BBB. *IB:* 32. Interview required.

B230 MPharm Pharmacy
Duration: 4FT Hon   CRB Check: Required
Entry Requirements: *GCE:* ABB. *IB:* 32. *BTEC NC:* DD. *BTEC ND:* DDM. Interview required.

K60 KING'S COLLEGE LONDON (UNIVERSITY OF LONDON)
STRAND
LONDON WC2R 2LS
t: 020 7848 7070 f: 020 7848 7171
e: prospective@kcl.ac.uk
// www.kcl.ac.uk

B210 BSc Pharmacology (3 years or 4-year sandwich)
Duration: 3FT Hon
Entry Requirements: *GCE:* AABc. *SQAH:* AAABB. *IB:* 36.

BC24 BSc Pharmacology and Molecular Genetics
Duration: 3FT Hon
Entry Requirements: *GCE:* AABc. *SQAH:* AABBB. *IB:* 36.

B230 MPharm Pharmacy (Master of) (4 years)
Duration: 4FT Hon   CRB Check: Required
Entry Requirements: *GCE:* AABc. *SQAH:* AAABB. *IB:* 36. *BTEC NC:* MM. Interview required.

K84 KINGSTON UNIVERSITY
STUDENT INFORMATION & ADVICE CENTRE
COOPER HOUSE
40-46 SURBITON ROAD
KINGSTON UPON THAMES KT1 2HX
t: 0844 8552177 f: 020 8547 7080
e: aps@kingston.ac.uk
// www.kingston.ac.uk

CB72 BSc Biochemistry and Pharmacology
Duration: 3FT Hon
Entry Requirements: Contact the institution for details.

CB7F BSc Biochemistry and Pharmacology
Duration: 4SW Hon
Entry Requirements: Contact the institution for details.

FB12 BSc Chemistry and Pharmacology
Duration: 4SW Hon
Entry Requirements: *GCE:* 200-280.

FB1F BSc Chemistry and Pharmacology
Duration: 3FT Hon
Entry Requirements: *GCE:* 200-280.

BB22 BSc Pharmaceutical Science
Duration: 3FT Hon
Entry Requirements: *GCE:* 200-280.

BBG2 BSc Pharmaceutical Science
Duration: 4SW Hon
Entry Requirements: *GCE:* 200-280.

B208 BSc Pharmaceutical Sciences (Foundation)
Duration: 4FT/5SW Hon
Entry Requirements: *GCE:* 60. Interview required.

B210 BSc Pharmacology
Duration: 3FT Hon
Entry Requirements: *GCE:* 200-280.

B211 BSc Pharmacology
Duration: 4SW Hon
Entry Requirements: *GCE:* 200-280.

B212 BSc Pharmacology (Foundation)
Duration: 4FT/5FT Hon
Entry Requirements: *GCE:* 60.

BN21 BSc Pharmacology and Business
Duration: 3FT Hon
Entry Requirements: *GCE:* 200-280.

BN2C BSc Pharmacology and Business
Duration: 4SW Hon
Entry Requirements: *GCE:* 200-280.

B2N1 BSc Pharmacology with Business
Duration: 3FT Hon
Entry Requirements: *GCE:* 200-280.

B2NC BSc Pharmacology with Business
Duration: 4SW Hon
Entry Requirements: *GCE:* 200-280.

B230 MPharm Pharmacy
Duration: 4FT Hon
Entry Requirements: *GCE:* 300. Interview required.

B204 MPharmSci Pharmaceutical Science (4-year FT)
Duration: 4FT Hon
Entry Requirements: *GCE:* 200-280.

BBF2 MPharmSci Pharmaceutical Sciences (with industrial placement)
Duration: 4FT Hon
Entry Requirements: *GCE:* 200-280.

L23 UNIVERSITY OF LEEDS
THE UNIVERSITY OF LEEDS
WOODHOUSE LANE
LEEDS LS2 9JT
t: 0113 343 3999
e: admissions@leeds.ac.uk
// www.leeds.ac.uk

B210 BSc Pharmacology
Duration: 3FT/4FT Hon
Entry Requirements: *GCE:* AAA-BBB. *SQAH:* AAAAA-AABBB. *SQAAH:* AAA-BBB. *BTEC ND:* DDD.

L41 THE UNIVERSITY OF LIVERPOOL
THE FOUNDATION BUILDING
BROWNLOW HILL
LIVERPOOL L69 7ZX
t: 0151 794 2000 f: 0151 708 6502
e: ugrecruitment@liv.ac.uk
// www.liv.ac.uk

F1B2 BSc Medicinal Chemistry
Duration: 3FT Hon
Entry Requirements: *GCE:* BBB. *SQAAH:* BBB. *IB:* 31.

B210 BSc Pharmacology
Duration: 3FT Hon
Entry Requirements: *GCE:* ABB-BBB. *SQAAH:* ABB-BBB. *IB:* 32. Interview required.

F1BF MChem Medicinal Chemistry with Pharmacology
Duration: 4FT Hon
Entry Requirements: *GCE:* ABB. *SQAAH:* ABB. *IB:* 33.

L51 LIVERPOOL JOHN MOORES UNIVERSITY
KINGSWAY HOUSE
HATTON GARDEN
LIVERPOOL L3 2AJ
t: 0151 231 5090 f: 0151 231 3462
e: courses@ljmu.ac.uk
// www.ljmu.ac.uk

B201 MPharm Pharmacy
Duration: 4FT Hon   CRB Check: Required
Entry Requirements: *GCE:* 300-320. *IB:* 26. *BTEC ND:* DDM. Interview required. Admissions Test required.

B230 MPharm Pharmacy (Collaborative Programme with MAHSA College Malaysia)
Duration: 4FT PMD
Entry Requirements: Contact the institution for details.

L68 LONDON METROPOLITAN UNIVERSITY
166-220 HOLLOWAY ROAD
LONDON N7 8DB
t: 020 7133 4200
e: admissions@londonmet.ac.uk
// www.londonmet.ac.uk

B230 BSc Pharmaceutical Science
Duration: 3FT Hon
Entry Requirements: *GCE:* 240. *IB:* 28.

B210 BSc Pharmacology
Duration: 3FT/4SW Hon
Entry Requirements: *GCE:* 240. *IB:* 28.

M20 THE UNIVERSITY OF MANCHESTER
OXFORD ROAD
MANCHESTER M13 9PL
t: 0161 275 2077 f: 0161 275 2106
e: ug-admissions@manchester.ac.uk
// www.manchester.ac.uk

B210 BSc Pharmacology
Duration: 3FT Hon
Entry Requirements: *GCE:* AAA-ABB. *SQAH:* AAAAA-AAABB. *SQAAH:* AAA-ABB. *BTEC ND:* DDM. Interview required.

B211 BSc Pharmacology with Industrial/Professional Experience (4 years)
Duration: 4SW Hon
Entry Requirements: *GCE:* AAA-ABB. *SQAH:* AAAAA-AAABB. *SQAAH:* AAA-ABB. *BTEC ND:* DDM. Interview required.

B212 BSc Pharmacology with a Modern Language (4 years)
Duration: 4FT Hon
Entry Requirements: *GCE:* AAA-ABB. *SQAH:* AAAAA-AAABB. *SQAAH:* AAA-ABB. *BTEC ND:* DDM. Interview required.

B230 MPharm Pharmacy
Duration: 4FT Hon
Entry Requirements: *GCE:* AAB-ABB. *SQAH:* AAABB-AABBB. *SQAAH:* BB. Interview required.

B231 MPharm Pharmacy with a Foundation Year
Duration: 5FT Hon
Entry Requirements: Contact the institution for details.

M62 MEDWAY SCHOOL OF PHARMACY
UNIVERSITY OF KENT
THE REGISTRY
CANTERBURY CT2 7NZ
t: 01227 827272 f: 01227 827077
e: recruitment@kent.ac.uk
// www.kent.ac.uk

B231 FdSc Pharmacy Practice
Duration: 2FT Fdg
Entry Requirements: *GCE:* CCC. *SQAH:* BBCCC. *SQAAH:* CCC. *IB:* 28. *BTEC ND:* MMM.

B230 MPharm Pharmacy
Duration: 4FT Hon
Entry Requirements: *GCE:* BBB. *SQAH:* AABBB. *SQAAH:* BBB. *IB:* 32. *BTEC ND:* DDM.

N21 NEWCASTLE UNIVERSITY
KING'S GATE
NEWCASTLE UPON TYNE NE1 7RU
t: 0191 208 3333 f: 0191 222 6143
// www.ncl.ac.uk

B210 BSc Pharmacology
Duration: 3FT Hon
Entry Requirements: *GCE:* AAB-BBB. *SQAH:* AAAB. *IB:* 32.

N84 THE UNIVERSITY OF NOTTINGHAM
THE ADMISSIONS OFFICE
THE UNIVERSITY OF NOTTINGHAM
UNIVERSITY PARK
NOTTINGHAM NG7 2RD
t: 0115 951 5151 f: 0115 951 4668
// www.nottingham.ac.uk

B230 MPharm Pharmacy (4 years)
Duration: 4FT Hon
Entry Requirements: *GCE:* AAB. *SQAAH:* AAB. *IB:* 36. Interview required.

N91 NOTTINGHAM TRENT UNIVERSITY
DRYDEN BUILDINGG
BURTON STREET
NOTTINGHAM NG1 4BU
t: +44 (0) 115 848 4200 f: +44 (0) 115 848 8869
e: applications@ntu.ac.uk
// www.ntu.ac.uk/

B210 BSc (Hons) Pharmacology
Duration: 3FT/4SW Hon
Entry Requirements: *GCE:* 280. *SQAH:* BBCCC. *SQAAH:* CCC. *IB:* 29. *BTEC NC:* DM. *BTEC ND:* DMM.

P80 UNIVERSITY OF PORTSMOUTH
ACADEMIC REGISTRY
UNIVERSITY HOUSE
WINSTON CHURCHILL AVENUE
PORTSMOUTH PO1 2UP
t: 023 9284 8484 f: 023 9284 3082
e: admissions@port.ac.uk
// www.port.ac.uk

B210 BSc Pharmacology
Duration: 3FT Hon
Entry Requirements: *GCE:* BCC. *IB:* 29. *BTEC ND:* DMM.

B230 MPharm Pharmacy
Duration: 4FT Hon   CRB Check: Required
Entry Requirements: *GCE:* ABB. *IB:* 31. *BTEC NC:* DD. *BTEC ND:* DDM. Interview required.

Q25 QUEEN MARGARET UNIVERSITY, EDINBURGH
QUEEN MARGARET UNIVERSITY DRIVE
EDINBURGH EH21 6UU
t: 0131474 0000 f: 0131 474 0001
e: admissions@qmu.ac.uk
// www.qmu.ac.uk

B210 BSc Applied Pharmacology
Duration: 4FT Hon
Entry Requirements: *GCE:* 160. *IB:* 26.

Q75 QUEEN'S UNIVERSITY BELFAST
UNIVERSITY ROAD
BELFAST BT7 1NN
t: 028 9097 3838 f: 028 9097 5151
e: admissions@qub.ac.uk
// www.qub.ac.uk

B230 MPharm Pharmacy
Duration: 4FT Hon   CRB Check: Required
Entry Requirements: *GCE:* AAB-ABBa. *IB:* 34. Interview required.

R12 THE UNIVERSITY OF READING
THE UNIVERSITY OF READING
PO BOX 217
READING RG6 6AH
t: 0118 378 8619 f: 0118 378 8924
e: student.recruitment@reading.ac.uk
// www.reading.ac.uk

B230 MPharm Pharmacy
Duration: 4FT Hon
Entry Requirements: *GCE:* AAB-ABB. *SQAH:* BBBBBB. *SQAAH:* BBB. Interview required.

R36 ROBERT GORDON UNIVERSITY
ROBERT GORDON UNIVERSITY
SCHOOLHILL
ABERDEEN
SCOTLAND AB10 1FR
t: 01224 26 27 28 f: 01224 26 21 47
e: UGOffice@rgu.ac.uk
// www.rgu.ac.uk

B230 MPharm Pharmacy
Duration: 4FT Hon   CRB Check: Required
Entry Requirements: *GCE:* 300. *SQAH:* AABB-BBBBC. *IB:* 32.

S12 THE SCHOOL OF PHARMACY (UNIVERSITY OF LONDON)
29-39 BRUNSWICK SQUARE
LONDON WC1N 1AX
t: 020 7753 5831 f: 020 7753 5829
e: registry@pharmacy.ac.uk
// www.pharmacy.ac.uk

B230 MPharm Master of Pharmacy (4 years)
Duration: 4FT Hon   CRB Check: Required
Entry Requirements: *GCE:* AAA-AAB. *SQAH:* AAABB. *SQAAH:* AB-BB. *IB:* 35. Interview required.

S21 SHEFFIELD HALLAM UNIVERSITY
CITY CAMPUS
HOWARD STREET
SHEFFIELD S1 1WB
t: 0114 225 5555 f: 0114 225 2167
e: admissions@shu.ac.uk
// www.shu.ac.uk

B230 BSc Pharmaceutical Sciences
Duration: 3FT/4SW Hon
Entry Requirements: *GCE:* 260.

S27 UNIVERSITY OF SOUTHAMPTON
HIGHFIELD
SOUTHAMPTON SO17 1BJ
t: 023 8059 4732 f: 023 8059 3037
e: admissions@soton.ac.uk
// www.southampton.ac.uk

B210 BSc Pharmacology
Duration: 3FT/4SW Hon
Entry Requirements: *GCE:* 300-340. *SQAAH:* AAB-BBB. *IB:* 32.

S78 THE UNIVERSITY OF STRATHCLYDE
GLASGOW G1 1XQ
t: 0141 552 4400 f: 0141 552 0775
// www.strath.ac.uk

CB72 BSc Biochemistry and Pharmacology (c)
Duration: 4FT Hon
Entry Requirements: *GCE:* BBB. *SQAH:* AAAC-ABBB. *IB:* 28.

CB92 BSc Immunology and Pharmacology (c)
Duration: 4FT Hon
Entry Requirements: *GCE:* BBB. *SQAH:* AAAC-ABBB. *IB:* 28.

B230 MPharm Pharmacy
Duration: 4FT Hon   CRB Check: Required
Entry Requirements: *GCE:* ABB. *SQAH:* ABBB. *IB:* 36.

B211 MSci Pharmacology
Duration: 5FT Hon
Entry Requirements: *GCE:* ABB. *SQAH:* AABBC-AABB. *IB:* 32.

S84 UNIVERSITY OF SUNDERLAND
STUDENT HELPLINE
THE STUDENT GATEWAY
CHESTER ROAD
SUNDERLAND SR1 3SD
t: 0191 515 3000 f: 0191 515 3805
e: student.helpline@sunderland.ac.uk
// www.sunderland.ac.uk

B230 MPharm Pharmacy
Duration: 4FT Hon   CRB Check: Required
Entry Requirements: *GCE:* 300-360. *SQAH:* AABBB. *SQAAH:* BBC.

S85 UNIVERSITY OF SURREY
STAG HILL
GUILDFORD
SURREY GU2 7XH
t: +44(0)1483 689305 f: +44(0)1483 689388
e: ugteam@surrey.ac.uk
// www.surrey.ac.uk

C7B2 BSc Biochemistry (Pharmacology) (3 or 4 years)
Duration: 3FT Hon
Entry Requirements: *GCE:* AAB-ABB. *SQAH:* AABBB-ABBBB. *BTEC ND:* DDD. Interview required.

U20 UNIVERSITY OF ULSTER
COLERAINE
CO. LONDONDERRY
NORTHERN IRELAND BT52 1SA
t: 028 7032 4221 f: 028 7032 4908
e: online@ulster.ac.uk
// www.ulster.ac.uk

B230 MPharm Pharmacy
Duration: 4FT Hon   CRB Check: Required
Entry Requirements: *GCE:* AAB. *SQAH:* AAAAB. *SQAAH:* AAB. *IB:* 37. *BTEC NC:* DD. *BTEC ND:* DDD.

U80 UNIVERSITY COLLEGE LONDON (UNIVERSITY OF LONDON)
GOWER STREET
LONDON WC1E 6BT
t: 020 7679 3000 f: 020 7679 3001
// www.ucl.ac.uk

B210 BSc Pharmacology
Duration: 3FT Hon
Entry Requirements: *GCE:* AAAe-AABe. *SQAAH:* AAA-AAB. Interview required.

B211 MSci Pharmacology
Duration: 4FT Hon
Entry Requirements: *GCE:* AAAe-AABe. *SQAAH:* AAA-AAB. Interview required.

W75 UNIVERSITY OF WOLVERHAMPTON
ADMISSIONS UNIT
MX207, CAMP STREET
WOLVERHAMPTON
WEST MIDLANDS WV1 1AD
t: 01902 321000 f: 01902 321896
e: admissions@wlv.ac.uk
// www.wlv.ac.uk

B200 BSc Human Biology
Duration: 3FT Hon
Entry Requirements: Contact the institution for details.

B230 BSc Pharmaceutical Science
Duration: 3FT Hon
Entry Requirements: *GCE:* 160-200. *IB:* 24.

B210 BSc Pharmacology
Duration: 3FT Hon
Entry Requirements: *GCE:* 160-200.

B231 MPharm Pharmacy
Duration: 4FT Hon   CRB Check: Required
Entry Requirements: *GCE:* 300-360. Interview required.

PS